Frederic P. Miller, Agnes F. Vandome,
John McBrewster (Ed.)

ADHD predominantly inattentive

D1736028

Frederic P. Miller, Agnes F. Vandome,
John McBrewster (Ed.)

ADHD predominantly inattentive

Attention-deficit Hyperactivity Disorder,
Diagnostic and Statistical Manual of Mental
Disorders, Adult Attention Deficit
Hyperactivity Disorder, Auditory Processing
Disorder, Chemical Imbalance.

Alphascript Publishing

Imprint

All parts of this book are extracted from Wikipedia, the free encyclopedia (www.wikipedia.org).

You can get detailed informations about the authors of this collection of articles at the end of this book. The editors (Ed.) of this book are no authors. They have not modified or extended the original texts.

Pictures published in this book can be under different licences than the GNU Free Documentation License. You can get detailed informations about the authors and licences of pictures at the end of this book.

The content of this book was generated collaboratively by volunteers. Please be advised that nothing found here has necessarily been reviewed by people with the expertise required to provide you with complete, accurate or reliable information. Some information in this book maybe misleading or wrong. The Publisher does not guarantee the validity of the information found here. If you need specific advice (f.e. in fields of medical, legal, financial, or risk management questions) please contact a professional who is licensed or knowledgeable in that area.

Cover image: www.PureStockX.com
Concerning the licence of the cover image please contact PureStockX.

Publisher:
Alphascript Publishing is a trademark of
VDM Publishing House Ltd.,17 Rue Meldrum, Beau Bassin,1713-01 Mauritius
Email: info@vdm-publishing-house.com
Website: www.vdm-publishing-house.com

Published in 2010

Printed in: U.S.A., U.K., Germany. This book was not produced in Mauritius.

ISBN: 978-613-0-28859-4

Contents

Articles

References

ADHD predominantly inattentive

ADHD predominantly inattentive (**ADHD-PI** or **ADHD-I**) is one of the three subtypes of → Attention-deficit hyperactivity disorder (ADHD).

While ADHD-PI is sometimes still called **attention deficit disorder** or **ADD** by the general public, these older terms were formally changed in 1994 in the new → Diagnostic and Statistical Manual of Mental Disorders, fourth edition (DSM-IV).

Differences from other ADHD subtypes

ADHD-PI is different from the other subtypes of ADHD in that it is characterized primarily by inattention, easy distractibility, disorganization, procrastination, forgetfulness, and lethargy (fatigue), but with less or none of the symptoms of hyperactivity or impulsiveness typical of the other ADHD subtypes.

Children with ADHD-PI are usually not diagnosed nearly as early as children with other ADHD subtypes, possibly because their lack of hyperactivity symptoms may make their condition less obvious to observers.[1] These children are at greater risk of academic failures and early withdrawal from school.[2] Teachers and parents may make incorrect assumptions about the behaviors and attitudes of a child with undiagnosed ADHD-PI, and may provide them with frequent and erroneous negative feedback (e.g. "you're irresponsible", "you're lazy", "you don't care/show any effort", "you just aren't trying", etc.).[3]

The more intelligent inattentive children may realize on some level that they are somehow different internally from their peers; however, they are unfortunately also likely to accept and internalize the continuous negative feedback, creating a negative self-image that becomes self-reinforcing. If these children progress into adulthood undiagnosed and untreated, their inattentiveness, ongoing frustrations, and poor self-image frequently create numerous and severe problems maintaining healthy relationships, succeeding in postsecondary schooling, or succeeding in the workplace. These problems can compound frustrations and low self-esteem, and will often lead to the development of secondary pathologies including anxiety disorders, mood disorders, and substance abuse.[2]

It has been suggested by Patricia Quinn.[1] , among others, that some of the symptoms of ADHD present in childhood appear to be less overt in adulthood. This is likely due to an adult's ability to make cognitive adjustments and develop coping skills minimizing the frequency of inattentive or hyperactive behaviors. However, the core problems of ADHD do not disappear with age.[2] Some researchers have suggested that individuals with reduced or less overt hyperactivity symptoms should receive the ADHD-combined diagnosis. Hallowell and Ratey (2005) suggest[4] that the manifestation of hyperactivity simply changes with adolescence and adulthood, becoming a more generalized restlessness or tendency to fidget.

In the DSM-III, sluggishness, drowsiness, and daydreaming were listed as characteristics of ADHD. The symptoms were removed from the ADHD criteria in DSM-IV because, although those with ADHD-PI were found to have these symptoms, this only occurred with the absence of hyperactive symptoms. These distinct symptoms were erroneously described as → sluggish cognitive tempo (SCT).

Some experts, such as Dr. Russell Barkley,[5] argue that ADHD-PI is so different from the other ADHD subtypes that it should be regarded as a distinct disorder. Barkley cites different symptoms among those with ADHD-PI -- particularly the almost complete lack of conduct disorders and high-risk, thrill-seeking behavior -- and markedly different responses to stimulant medication.

Symbols

except for :
Hockey
Guitar

DSM-IV criteria

The → DSM-IV allows for diagnosis of the *predominantly inattentive* subtype of ADHD (under code 314.00) if the individual presents six or more of the following symptoms of inattention for at least six months to a point that is disruptive and inappropriate for developmental level:

- Often does not give close attention to details or makes careless mistakes in schoolwork, work, or other activities.
- Often has trouble keeping attention on tasks or play activities.
- Often does not seem to listen when spoken to directly.
- Often does not follow instructions and fails to finish schoolwork, chores, or duties in the workplace (not due to oppositional behavior or failure to understand instructions).
- Often has trouble organizing activities.
- Often avoids, dislikes, or doesn't want to do things that take a lot of mental effort for a long period of time (such as schoolwork or homework).
- Often loses things needed for tasks and activities (e.g. toys, school assignments, pencils, books, or tools).
- Is often easily distracted.
- Is often forgetful in daily activities.

A requirement for an ADHD-PI diagnosis is that of the symptoms that cause impairment must be present in two or more settings (e.g., at school or work and at home). There must also be clear evidence of clinically significant impairment in social, academic, or occupational functioning. Lastly, the symptoms must not occur exclusively during the course of a pervasive developmental disorder, schizophrenia, or other psychotic disorder, and are not better accounted for by another mental disorder (e.g., mood disorder, anxiety disorder, dissociative disorder, personality disorder).

School
7
Delinda

Examples of observed symptoms

Life Period	Example
Children [6]	Failing to pay close attention to details or making careless mistakes when doing schoolwork or other activities
	Trouble keeping attention focused during play or tasks *ping·pong*
	Appearing not to listen when spoken to (often being accused of "daydreaming")
	Failing to follow instructions or finish tasks
	Avoiding tasks that require a high amount of mental effort and organization, such as school projects
	Frequently losing items required to facilitate tasks or activities, such as school supplies
	Excessive distractibility
	Forgetfulness
	Procrastination, inability to begin an activity
	Difficulties completing household chores

Adults[7]	Often making careless mistakes when having to work on uninteresting or difficult projects
	Often having difficulty keeping attention during work, or holding down a job for a significant amount of time
	Often having difficulty concentrating on conversations
	Having trouble finishing projects that have already been started
	Often having difficulty organizing for the completion of tasks
	Avoiding or delaying in starting projects that require a lot of thought
	Often misplacing or having difficulty finding things at home or at work
	Disorganized personal items (sometimes old and useless to the individual) causing excessive "clutter" (in the home, car, etc)
	Often distracted by activity or noise
	Often having problems remembering appointments or obligations, or inconveniently changing plans on a regular basis

See also

- → Attention-deficit hyperactivity disorder for main article
- Adult attention-deficit disorder
- → Auditory processing disorder
- Chemical imbalance theory
- → Educational psychology
- → School psychology
- Sensory integration disorder
- → Sluggish cognitive tempo
- → Wilson's syndrome

References

[1] Quinn, Patricia (1994). *ADD and the College Student: A Guide for High School and College Students with Attention Deficit Disorder* (http://www.maginationpress.com/4416630.html). New York, NY: Magination Press. pp. 2–3. ISBN 1-55798-663-0. .

[2] Triolo, Santo (1998). *Attention Deficit Hyperactivity Disorder in Adulthood: A Practitioner's Handbook* (http://www.ilab.org/db/detail.php?booknr=338314075). Philadelphia, PA: Brunner-Routledge. pp. 65–69. ISBN 0-87630-890-6. .

[3] Kelly, Kate; Peggy Ramundo (2006). *You Mean I'm Not Lazy, Stupid or Crazy?! The Classic Self-Help Book For Adults with Attention Deficit Disorder* (http://www.simonsays.com/content/book.cfm?tab=1&pid=506364). New York, NY: Scribner. pp. 11–12. ISBN 0-7432-6448-7. .

[4] Hallowell, Edward M. and John J. Ratey (2005). Delivered from Distraction : Getting the Most out of Life with Attention Deficit Disorder. New York: Ballantine Books, p. 253–5. ISBN 0-345-44231-8

[5] "Russell Barkley on AD/HD" (http://www.schwablearning.org/pdfs/2200_7-barktran.pdf?date=4-12-05) (2000)

[6] What we know (http://www.help4adhd.org/en/about/what/WWK1) National Resource Center on AD/HD

[7] WHO adult AD/HD inattentive symptoms (http://www.help4adhd.org/documents/WWK8.pdf) National Resource Center on ADHD

External links

- http://www.adda-sr.org/reading/Articles/mooreinattentive.htm
- http://www.psychnet-uk.com/readers_articles/adhd_general.htm
- http://www.aqeta.qc.ca/english/general/types/23.htm
- http://www.cwgsy.net/community/mindinfo/add/addi.htm
- http://www.goaskmom.com

Attention-deficit hyperactivity disorder

Attention-deficit hyperactivity disorder	
Classification and external resources	
ICD-10	F f90.htm+ f90 90 . [1]
ICD-9	314.00 [2], 314.01 [3]
OMIM	143465 [4]
DiseasesDB	6158 [5]
MedlinePlus	001551 [6]
eMedicine	med/3103 [7] ped/177 [8]
MeSH	D001289 [9]

Attention-deficit hyperactivity disorder (**ADHD** or **AD/HD**) is a neurobehavioral[10] developmental disorder.[11] ADHD is primarily characterized by "the co-existence of attentional problems and hyperactivity, with each behavior occurring infrequently alone."[12] While symptoms may appear to be innocent and merely annoying nuisances to observers, "if left untreated, the persistent and pervasive effects of ADHD symptoms can insidiously and severely interfere with one's ability to get the most out of education, fulfill one's potential in the workplace, establish and maintain interpersonal relationships, and maintain a generally positive sense of self."[13] p.2

ADHD is the most commonly studied and diagnosed psychiatric disorder in children, affecting about 3 to 5% of children globally with symptoms starting before seven years of age.[14] [15] ADHD is a common chronic disorder in children[16] with 30 to 50% of those individuals diagnosed in childhood continuing to have symptoms into adulthood.[17] [18] Adolescents and adults with ADHD tend to develop coping mechanisms to compensate for some or all of their impairments.[19] However, many aspects of daily life that most people take for granted are rendered more difficult by the symptoms of ADHD.[13]

Though previously regarded as a childhood diagnosis, ADHD can continue throughout adulthood.[20] 4.7 percent of American adults are estimated to live with ADHD.[21] ADHD is diagnosed two to four times as frequently in boys as in girls,[22] [23] though studies suggest this discrepancy may be due to subjective bias of referring teachers.[24] ADHD management usually involves some combination of medications, behavior modifications, lifestyle changes, and counseling. Its symptoms can be difficult to differentiate from other disorders, increasing the likelihood that the diagnosis of ADHD will be missed[13] or vice versa. Additionally, most clinicians have not received formal training in the assessment and treatment of ADHD, particularly in adult patients.[13]

ADHD and its diagnosis and treatment have been considered controversial since the 1970s.[25] The controversies have involved clinicians, teachers, policymakers, parents and the media. Opinions regarding ADHD range from not believing it exists at all to believing there are genetic and physiological bases for the condition as well as disagreement about the use of stimulant medications in treatment.[26] [27] [28] Most healthcare providers accept that ADHD is a genuine disorder with debate in the scientific community centering mainly around how it is diagnosed and treated.[29] [30] [31] The AMA Council on Scientific Affairs concluded in 1998 that "(d)iagnostic criteria for ADHD are based on extensive empirical research and, if applied appropriately, lead to the diagnosis of a syndrome with high interrater reliability, good face validity, and high predictability of course and medication responsiveness."[32]

- meds
- CBT · Behavior Mods
- lifestyle changes
- Counseling

Development lag : Behavior Disorder

NOT a neurological disease

Classification

ADHD may be seen as one or more continuous traits found normally throughout the general population.[33] ADHD is a developmental disorder in which certain traits such as impulse control lag in development.[34] Using magnetic resonance imaging of the prefrontal cortex, this developmental lag has been estimated to range from 3 to 5 years.[35] These delays are considered to cause impairment. ADHD has also been classified as a behavior disorder.[36] A diagnosis of ADHD does not, however, imply a neurological disease.[33]

ADHD is classified as a disruptive behavior disorder along with oppositional defiant disorder, conduct disorder and antisocial disorder.[37]

Subtypes

ADHD has three subtypes:[38]

- Predominantly hyperactive-impulsive
    - Most symptoms (six or more) are in the hyperactivity-impulsivity categories.
    - Fewer than six symptoms of inattention are present, although inattention may still be present to some degree.
- → Predominantly inattentive
    - The majority of symptoms (six or more) are in the inattention category and fewer than six symptoms of hyperactivity-impulsivity are present, although hyperactivity-impulsivity may still be present to some degree.
    - Children with this subtype are less likely to act out or have difficulties getting along with other children. They may sit quietly, but they are not paying attention to what they are doing. Therefore, the child may be overlooked, and parents and teachers may not notice symptoms of ADHD.
- Combined hyperactive-impulsive and inattentive
    - Six or more symptoms of inattention and six or more symptoms of hyperactivity-impulsivity are present.
    - Most children with ADHD have the combined type.

Childhood ADHD

Attention-deficit hyperactivity disorder or ADHD is a common childhood illness that can be treated. It is a health condition involving biologically active substances in the brain. ADHD may affect certain areas of the brain that allow problem solving, planning ahead, understanding others' actions, and impulse control.[39]

The American Academy of Child Adolescent Psychiatry (AACAP) considers it necessary that the following be present before attaching the label of ADHD to a child:

- The behaviors must appear before age 7.
- They must continue for at least six months.
- The symptoms must also create a real handicap in at least two of the following areas of the child's life:
    - in the classroom,
    - on the playground,
    - at home,
    - in the community, or
    - in social settings.[39]

If a child seems too active on the playground but not elsewhere, the problem might not be ADHD. It might also not be ADHD if the behaviors occur in the classroom but nowhere else. A child who shows some symptoms would not be diagnosed with ADHD if his or her schoolwork or friendships are not impaired by the behaviors.[39]

Even if a child's behavior seems like ADHD, it might not actually be ADHD; careful attention to the process of differential diagnosis is mandatory. Many other conditions and situations can trigger behavior that resembles ADHD. For example, a child might show ADHD symptoms when experiencing:

- A death or divorce in the family, a parent's job loss, or other sudden change
- Undetected seizures **?**
- An ear infection that causes temporary hearing problems
- Problems with schoolwork caused by a learning disability
- Anxiety or depression[39]   ———————→   *where we got a diagnosis for Andrew*
- Insufficient or poor quality sleep
- Child abuse

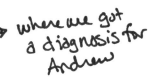

Adult ADHD

It has been estimated that about eight million adults have ADHD in the United States.[40] Untreated adults with ADHD often have chaotic lifestyles, may appear to be disorganized and may rely on non-prescribed drugs and alcohol to get by.[41] They often have such associated psychiatric comorbidities as depression, anxiety disorder, bipolar disorder, substance abuse, or a learning disability.[41] A diagnosis of ADHD may offer adults insight into their behaviors and allow patients to become more aware and seek help with coping and treatment strategies.[40] There is controversy amongst some experts on whether ADHD persists into adulthood. Recognized as occurring in adults in 1978, it is currently not addressed separately from ADHD in childhood. Obstacles that clinicians face when assessing adults who may have ADHD include developmentally inappropriate diagnostic criteria, age-related changes, comorbidities and the possibility that high intelligence or situational factors can mask ADHD.[42]

Symptoms

Inattention, hyperactivity, and impulsivity are the key behaviors of ADHD. The symptoms of ADHD are especially difficult to define because it is hard to draw the line at where normal levels of inattention, hyperactivity, and impulsivity end and clinically significant levels requiring intervention begin.[13] To be diagnosed with the disorder, a child must have symptoms for 6 or more months and to a degree that is greater than other children of the same age.

The symptom categories of ADHD in children yield three potential classifications of ADHD—predominantly inattentive type, predominantly hyperactive-impulsive type, or combined type if criteria for both subtypes are met:[13] :p.4

Predominantly inattentive type symptoms may include:[43]

- Be easily distracted, miss details, forget things, and frequently switch from one activity to another
- Have difficulty focusing on one thing
- Become bored with a task after only a few minutes, unless they are doing something enjoyable
- Have difficulty focusing attention on organizing and completing a task or learning something new
- Have trouble completing or turning in homework assignments, often losing things (e.g., pencils, toys, assignments) needed to complete tasks or activities
- Not seem to listen when spoken to
- Daydream, become easily confused, and move slowly
- Have difficulty processing information as quickly and accurately as others
- Struggle to follow instructions.

Predominantly hyperactive-impulsive type symptoms may include:[43]   **— NO —**

- Fidget and squirm in their seats
- Talk nonstop
- Dash around, touching or playing with anything and everything in sight
- Have trouble sitting still during dinner, school, and story time
- Be constantly in motion
- Have difficulty doing quiet tasks or activities.

and also these manifestations primarily of impulsivity:[43]

- Be very impatient
- Blurt out inappropriate comments, show their emotions without restraint, and act without regard for consequences
- Have difficulty waiting for things they want or waiting their turns in games

Most people exhibit some of these behaviors, but not to the degree where such behaviors significantly interfere with a person's work, relationships, or studies. The core impairments are consistent even in different cultural contexts.[44]

Symptoms may persist into adulthood for up to half of children diagnosed with ADHD. Estimating this is difficult as there are no official diagnostic criteria for ADHD in adults.[13]

A 2009 study found that children with ADHD move around a lot because it helps them stay alert enough to complete challenging tasks.[45]

ADHD and other medical conditions

ADHD may accompany other disorders such as anxiety or depression. Such combinations can greatly complicate diagnosis and treatment. Academic studies and research in private practice suggest that depression in ADHD appears to be increasingly prevalent in children as they get older, with a higher rate of increase in girls than in boys, and to vary in prevalence with the subtype of ADHD. Where a mood disorder complicates ADHD it would be prudent to treat the mood disorder first, but parents of children who have ADHD often wish to have the ADHD treated first, because the response to treatment is quicker.[46]

Inattention and "hyperactive" behavior are not the only problems in children with ADHD. ADHD exists alone in only about 1/3 of the children diagnosed with it. Many co-existing conditions require other courses of treatment and should be diagnosed separately instead of being grouped in the ADHD diagnosis. Some of the associated conditions are:

- Oppositional defiant disorder (35%) and conduct disorder (26%) which both are characterized by anti-social behaviors such as stubbornness, aggression, frequent temper tantrums, deceitfulness, lying, or stealing.[47]
- Primary disorder of vigilance, which is characterized by poor attention and concentration, as well as difficulties staying awake. These children tend to fidget, yawn and stretch and appear to be hyperactive in order to remain alert and active.[47]
- Mood disorders. Boys diagnosed with the combined subtype have been shown likely to suffer from a mood disorder.[48]
- Bipolar disorder. As many as 25% of children with ADHD have bipolar disorder. Children with this combination may demonstrate more aggression and behavioral problems than those with ADHD alone.[47]
- Anxiety disorder, which has been found to be common in girls diagnosed with the inattentive subtype of ADHD.[49]
- Obsessive-compulsive disorder. OCD is believed to share a genetic component with ADHD and shares many of its characteristics.[47]

Causes

A specific cause of ADHD is not known.[50] There are, however, a number of factors that may contribute to ADHD. They include genetics, diet and social and physical environments.

Genetic factors

Twin studies indicate that the disorder is highly heritable and that genetics are a factor in about 75% of ADHD cases.[33] Hyperactivity also seems to be primarily a genetic condition; however, other causes do have an effect.[51]

Researchers believe that a large majority of ADHD cases arise from a combination of various genes, many of which affect dopamine transporters. Candidate genes include dopamine transporter, dopamine receptors D_2/D_3,[52] dopamine beta-hydroxylase monoamine oxidase A, catecholamine-methyl transferase, serotonin transporter promoter (SLC6A4), 5-hydroxytryptamine 2A receptor (5-HT2A), 5-hydroxytryptamine 1B receptor (5-HT1B),[53] the 10-repeat allele of the DAT1 gene,[54] the 7-repeat allele of the DRD4 gene,[54] and the dopamine beta hydroxylase gene (DBH TaqI).[55]

The broad selection of targets indicates that ADHD does not follow the traditional model of "a genetic disease" and should therefore be viewed as a complex interaction among genetic and environmental factors. Even though all these genes might play a role, to date no single gene has been shown to make a major contribution to ADHD.[56]

Evolutionary theories

The hunter vs. farmer theory is a hypothesis proposed by author Thom Hartmann about the origins of ADHD. The theory proposes that hyperactivity may be an adaptive behavior in pre modern humans[57] and that those with ADHD retain some of the older "hunter" characteristics associated with early pre-agricultural human society. According to this theory, individuals with ADHD may be more adept at searching and seeking and less adept at staying put and managing complex tasks over time.[58] Further evidence showing hyperactivity may be evolutionarily beneficial was put forth in 2006 in a study which found it may carry specific benefits for a society.[59]

Environmental factors

Twin studies to date have also suggested that approximately 9% to 20% of the variance in hyperactive-impulsive-inattentive behavior or ADHD symptoms can be attributed to nonshared environmental (nongenetic) factors.[60] [61] [62] [63]

Environmental factors implicated include alcohol and tobacco smoke exposure during pregnancy and environmental exposure to lead in very early life.[64] The relation of smoking to ADHD could be due to nicotine causing hypoxia (lack of oxygen) to the fetus *in utero*.[65] It could also be that women with ADHD are more likely to smoke[66] and therefore, due to the strong genetic component of ADHD, are more likely to have children with ADHD.[67] Complications during pregnancy and birth—including premature birth—might also play a role.[68] ADHD patients have been observed to have higher than average rates of head injuries;[69] however, current evidence does not indicate that head injuries are the cause of ADHD in the patients observed.[70]

Diet

A study[71] conducted by researchers at Southampton University in the United Kingdom and published in The Lancet on November 3, 2007 found a definitive link between children's ingestion of many commonly used artificial food colors, the preservative sodium benzoate and hyperactivity. In response to these findings, the British government took prompt action. According to the Food Standards Agency, the food regulatory agency in the UK, food manufacturers are being encouraged to voluntarily phase out the use of most artificial food colors by the end of 2009. Following the FSA's actions, the European Commission ruled that any food products containing the "Southampton Six" (The contentious colourings are: sunset yellow FCF (E110), quinoline yellow (E104), carmoisine (E122), allura red (E129), tartrazine (E102) and ponceau 4R (E124)) must display warning labels on their packaging by 2010. In the US, little has been done to curb food manufacturer's use of artificial food colors, despite the new evidence presented by the Southampton study. However, the existing US Food Drug and Cosmetic Act[72] had already required that artificial food colors be approved for use, that they must be given FD&C numbers by the FDA, and the use of these colors must be indicated on the package.[73] This is why food packaging in the USA may state something like: "Contains FD&C Red #40."

Social factors

There is no compelling evidence that social factors alone can cause ADHD.[34] However, many researchers believe that relationships with caregivers have a profound effect on attentional and self-regulatory abilities. A study of foster children found that a high number of them had symptoms closely resembling ADHD.[74] Researchers have found behavior typical of ADHD in children who have suffered violence and emotional abuse.[33] [75] Furthermore, Complex Post Traumatic Stress Disorder can result in attention problems that can look like ADHD.[76] ADHD is also considered to be related to → sensory integration dysfunction.[77]

Neurodiversity

Proponents of the neurodiversity theory assert that atypical (neurodivergent) neurological development is a normal human difference that is to be tolerated and respected just like any other human difference. Social critics argue that while biological factors may play a large role in difficulties with sitting still in class and/or concentrating on schoolwork in some children, these children could have failed to integrate others' social expectations of their behavior for a variety of other reasons.[78] It has been said that ADHD has a link with creativity.[79] As genetic research into ADHD proceeds, it may become possible to integrate this information with the neurobiology in order to distinguish disability from varieties of normal or even exceptional functioning in people along the same spectrum of attention differences.[80]

Social construct theory of ADHD

Social construction theory states that it is societies that determine where the line between normal and abnormal behavior is drawn. Thus society members including physicians, parents, teachers, and others are the ones who determine which diagnostic criteria are applied and thus determine the number of people affected.[81] This is exemplified in the fact that the DSM IV arrives at levels of ADHD three to four times higher than those obtained with use of the ICD 10.[23] Thomas Szasz, an extreme proponent of this theory, has gone so far as to state that ADHD was "invented and not discovered."[82] [83]

Low arousal theory

According to the low arousal theory, people with ADHD need excessive activity as self-stimulation because of their state of abnormally low arousal.[84] [85] The theory states that those with ADHD cannot self-moderate, and their attention can only be gained by means of environmental stimuli,[84] which in turn results in disruption of attentional capacity and an increase in hyperactive behaviour.[86]

Without enough stimulation coming from the environment, an ADHD child will create it him or herself by walking around, fidgeting, talking, etc. This theory also explains why stimulant medications have high success rates and can induce a calming effect at therapeutic dosages among children with ADHD. It establishes a strong link with scientific data that ADHD is connected to abnormalities with the neurochemical dopamine and a powerful link with low-stimulation PET scan results in ADHD subjects.[84]

Pathophysiology

The pathophysiology of ADHD is unclear and there are a number of competing theories.[87] Research on children with ADHD has shown a general reduction of brain volume, but with a proportionally greater reduction in the volume of the left-sided prefrontal cortex. These findings suggest that the core ADHD features of inattention, hyperactivity, and impulsivity may reflect frontal lobe dysfunction, but other brain regions particularly the cerebellum have also been implicated.[88] Neuroimaging studies in ADHD have not always given consistent results and as of 2008 are only used for research not

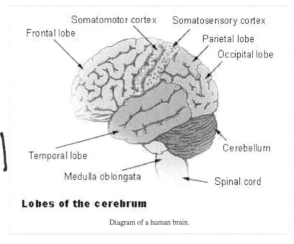

Lobes of the cerebrum

Diagram of a human brain.

diagnostic purposes.[89] A 2005 review of published studies involving neuroimaging, neuropsychological genetics, and neurochemistry found converging lines of evidence to suggest that four connected frontostriatal regions play a role in the pathophysiology of ADHD: The lateral prefrontal cortex, dorsal anterior cingulate cortex, caudate, and putamen.[90]

In one study a delay in development of certain brain structures by an average of three years occurred in ADHD elementary school aged patients. The delay was most prominent in the frontal cortex and temporal lobe, which are believed to be responsible for the ability to control and focus thinking. In contrast, the motor cortex in the ADHD patients was seen to mature faster than normal, suggesting that both slower development of behavioral control and advanced motor development might be required for the fidgetiness that characterizes ADHD.[91] It should be noted that stimulant medication itself may affect growth factors of the central nervous system.[92]

The same laboratory had previously found involvement of the "7-repeat" variant of the dopamine D4 receptor gene, which accounts for about 30 percent of the genetic risk for ADHD, in unusual thinness of the cortex of the right side of the brain; however, in contrast to other variants of the gene found in ADHD patients, the region normalized in thickness during the teen years in these children, coinciding with clinical improvement.[93]

Additionally, SPECT scans found people with ADHD to have reduced blood circulation (indicating low neural activity),[94] and a significantly higher concentration of dopamine transporters in the striatum which is in charge of planning ahead.[95] [96] A study by the U.S. Department of Energy's Brookhaven National Laboratory in collaboration with Mount Sinai School of Medicine in New York suggest that it is not the dopamine transporter levels that indicate ADHD, but the brain's ability to produce dopamine itself. The study was done by injecting 20 ADHD subjects and 25 control subjects with a radiotracer that attaches itself to dopamine transporters. The study found that it was not the transporter levels that indicated ADHD, but the dopamine itself. ADHD subjects showed lower levels of dopamine across the board. They speculated that since ADHD subjects had lower levels of dopamine to begin with, the number of transporters in the brain was not the telling factor. In support of this notion, plasma homovanillic acid, an index of dopamine levels, was found to be inversely related not only to childhood ADHD symptoms in adult psychiatric patients, but to "childhood learning problems" in healthy subjects as well.[97]

A 1990 PET scan study by Alan J. Zametkin *et al.* found that global cerebral glucose metabolism was 8% lower in medication-naive adults who had been hyperactive since childhood.[98] Further studies found that chronic stimulant treatment had little effect on global glucose metabolism,[99] a 1993 study in girls failed to find a decreased global glucose metabolism, but found significant differences in glucose metabolism in 6 specific regions of the brains of ADHD girls as compared to control subjects. The study also found that differences in one specific region of the frontal lobe were statistically correlated with symptom severity.[100] A further study in 1997 also failed to find global differences in glucose metabolism, but similarly found differences in glucose normalization in specific regions of the brain. The 1997 study also noted that their findings were somewhat different than those in the 1993 study, and concluded that sexual maturation may have played a role in this discrepancy.[101] The significance of the research by Zametkin has not been determined and neither his group nor any other has been able to replicate the 1990 results.[102] [103] [104]

Critics, such as Jonathan Leo and David Cohen, who reject the characterization of ADHD as a disorder, contend that the controls for stimulant medication usage were inadequate in some lobar volumetric studies which makes it impossible to determine whether ADHD itself or psychotropic medication used to treat ADHD is responsible for the decreased thickness observed[105] in certain brain regions. While the main study in question used age-matched controls, it did not provide information on height and weight of the subjects. These variables it has been argued could account for the regional brain size differences rather than ADHD itself.[106] [107] They believe many neuroimaging studies are oversimplified in both popular and scientific discourse and given undue weight despite deficiencies in experimental methodology.[106]

Diagnosis

ADHD is diagnosed via a psychiatric assessment; to rule out other potential causes or comorbidities, physical examination, radiological imaging, and laboratory tests may be used.[108]

In North America, the DSM-IV criteria are often the basis for a diagnosis, while European countries usually use the ICD-10.[109] If the DSM-IV criteria is used rather than the ICD-10 a diagnosis ADHD is 3–4 times more likely.[23] Factors other than those within the DSM or ICD however have been found to effect the diagnosis in clinical practice. A child's social and school environment as well as academic pressures at school are likely to be of influence.[110]

Many of the symptoms of ADHD occur from time to time in everyone; in patients with ADHD, the frequency of these symptoms is greater and patients' lives are significantly impaired. Impairment must occur in multiple settings to be classified as ADHD. As with many other psychiatric and medical disorders, the formal diagnosis is made by a qualified professional in the field based on a set number of criteria. In the USA these criteria are laid down by the American Psychiatric Association in their Diagnostic and Statistical Manual of Mental Disorders (DSM-IV), 4th edition. Based on the DSM-IV criteria listed below, three types of ADHD are classified:

1. ADHD, Combined Type: if both criteria 1A and 1B are met for the past 6 months
2. → ADHD Predominantly Inattentive Type: if criterion 1A is met but criterion 1B is not met for the past six months
3. ADHD, Predominantly Hyperactive-Impulsive Type: if criterion 1B is met but criterion 1A is not met for the past six months.

The previously used term *ADD* expired with the most recent revision of the DSM. Consequently, ADHD is the current nomenclature used to describe the disorder as one distinct disorder which can manifest itself as being a primary deficit resulting in hyperactivity/impulsivity (ADHD, predominately hyperactive-impulsive type) or inattention (ADHD predominately inattentive type) or both (ADHD combined type).

DSM-IV criteria

I. Either A or B:[111]

EITHER

(**A.**) Six or more of the following signs of inattention have been present for at least 6 months to a point that is disruptive and inappropriate for developmental level:

- *Inattentive:*

1. Often does not give close attention to details or makes careless mistakes in schoolwork, work, or other activities.
2. Often has trouble keeping attention on tasks or play activities.
3. Often does not seem to listen when spoken to directly.
4. Often does not follow instructions and fails to finish schoolwork, chores, or duties in the workplace (not due to oppositional behavior or failure to understand instructions).
5. Often has trouble organizing activities.
6. Often avoids, dislikes, or doesn't want to do things that take a lot of mental effort for a long period of time (such as schoolwork or homework).
7. Often loses things needed for tasks and activities (such as toys, school assignments, pencils, books, or tools).
8. Is often easily distracted.
9. Often forgetful in daily activities.

OR

(**B.**) Six or more of the following signs of hyperactivity-impulsivity have been present for at least 6 months to an extent that is disruptive and inappropriate for developmental level:

- *Hyperactivity:*

1. Often fidgets with hands or feet or squirms in seat.
2. Often gets up from seat when remaining in seat is expected.
3. Often runs about or climbs when and where it is not appropriate (adolescents or adults may feel very restless).
4. Often has trouble playing or enjoying leisure activities quietly.
5. Is often "on the go" or often acts as if "driven by a motor".
6. Often talks excessively.

- *Impulsiveness:*

1. Often blurts out answers before questions have been finished.
2. Often has trouble waiting one's turn.
3. Often interrupts or intrudes on others (example: butts into conversations or games).

II. Some signs that cause impairment were present before age 7 years.

III. Some impairment from the signs is present in two or more settings (such as at school/work and at home).

IV. There must be clear evidence of significant impairment in social, school, or work functioning.

V. The signs do not happen only during the course of a Pervasive Developmental Disorder, Schizophrenia, or other Psychotic Disorder. The signs are not better accounted for by another mental disorder (such as Mood Disorder, Anxiety Disorder, Dissociative Identity Disorder, or a Personality Disorder).

ICD-10

In the tenth edition of the *International Statistical Classification of Diseases and Related Health Problems* (ICD-10) the signs of ADHD are given the name "Hyperkinetic disorders". When a conduct disorder (as defined by ICD-10[112]) is present, the condition is referred to as "Hyperkinetic conduct disorder". Otherwise the disorder is classified as "Disturbance of Activity and Attention", "Other Hyperkinetic Disorders" or "Hyperkinetic Disorders, Unspecified". The latter is sometimes referred to as, "Hyperkinetic Syndrome".[112]

Other diagnostic guidelines

The American Academy of Pediatrics Clinical Practice Guideline for children with ADHD emphasizes that a reliable diagnosis is dependent upon the fulfillment of three criteria:[113]

- The use of explicit criteria for the diagnosis using the DSM-IV-TR.
- The importance of obtaining information about the child's signs in more than one setting.
- The search for coexisting conditions that may make the diagnosis more difficult or complicate treatment planning.

All three criteria are determined using the patient's history given by the parents, teachers and/or the patient.

Adults often continue to be impaired by ADHD. Adults with ADHD are diagnosed under the same criteria, including the stipulation that their signs must have been present prior to the age of seven.[111] Adults face some of their greatest challenges in the areas of self-control and self-motivation, as well as executive functioning, usually having more signs of inattention and fewer of hyperactivity or impulsiveness than children do.[114]

Comorbid conditions

Common comorbid conditions include oppositional defiant disorder (ODD). About 20% to 25% of children with ODD meet criteria for a learning disorder.[115] Learning disorders are more common when there are inattention signs.[116]

Comorbid disorders or substance abuse can make the diagnosis and treatment of ADHD more difficult. Psychosocial therapy is useful in treating some comorbid conditions.[117] ADHD is not, in boys, associated with increased substance misuse unless there is comorbid conduct disorder; but "research needs to examine the extent to which ADHD in adulthood increases the risk of substance use disorders."[118]

- Depression may also coincide with ADHD, increasingly prevalent among girls and older children.[46]

Epilepsy is a commonly found comorbid disorder in ADHD diagnosed individuals. Some forms of epilepsy can also cause ADHD like behaviour which can be misdiagnosed as ADHD.[119] [120]

Differential diagnoses

To make the diagnosis of ADHD, a number of other possible medical and psychological conditions must be excluded.

Medical conditions

Medical conditions that must be excluded include: hypothyroidism, anemia, lead poisoning, chronic illness, hearing or vision impairment, substance abuse, medication side effects, sleep impairment and child abuse, among others.[121]

Sleep conditions

As with other psychological and neurological issues, the relationship between ADHD and sleep is complex. In addition to clinical observations, there is substantial empirical evidence from a neuroanatomic standpoint to suggest that there is considerable overlap in the central nervous system centers that regulate sleep and those that regulate attention/arousal.[122] Primary sleep disorders play a role in the clinical presentation of symptoms of inattention and behavioral dysregulation. There are multilevel and bidirectional relationships among sleep, neurobehavioral functioning and the clinical syndrome of ADHD.[123]

Behavioral manifestations of sleepiness in children range from the classic ones (yawning, rubbing eyes), to externalizing behaviors (impulsivity, hyperactivity, aggressiveness), to mood lability and inattentiveness.[122] [124] Many sleep disorders are important causes of symptoms which may overlap with the cardinal symptoms of ADHD; children with ADHD should be regularly and systematically assessed for sleep problems.[122] [125]

From a clinical standpoint, mechanisms that account for the phenomenon of excessive daytime sleepiness include:

- Chronic sleep deprivation, that is insufficient sleep for physiologic sleep needs,
- Fragmented or disrupted sleep, caused by, for example, obstructive sleep apnea (OSA) or periodic limb movement disorder (PLMD),
- Primary clinical disorders of excessive daytime sleepiness, such as narcolepsy and
- Circadian rhythm disorders, such as delayed sleep phase syndrome (DSPS). A study in the Netherlands compared two groups of unmedicated 6-12-year-olds, all of them with "rigorously diagnosed ADHD". 87 of them had problems getting to sleep, 33 had no sleep problems. The larger group had a significantly later dim light melatonin onset (DLMO) than did the children with no sleep problems.[126]

Management

Methods of treatment often involve some combination of behavior modification, life-style changes, counseling, and medication. A 2005 study found that medical management and behavioral treatment is the most effective ADHD management strategy, followed by medication alone, and then behavioral treatment.[127] While medication has been shown to improve behavior when taken over the short term, they have not been shown to alter long term outcomes.[128]

Behavioral interventions

A 2009 review concluded that the evidence is strong for the effectiveness of behavioral treatments in ADHD.[129]

Psychological therapies used to treat ADHD include psychoeducational input, behavior therapy, cognitive behavioral therapy (CBT), interpersonal psychotherapy (IPT), family therapy, school-based interventions, social skills training and parent management training.[33]

Parent training and education have been found to have short term benefits.[130] Family therapy has shown to be of little use in the treatment of ADHD,[131] though it may be worth noting that parents of children with ADHD are more likely to divorce than parents of children without ADHD, particularly when their children are younger than eight years old.[132]

Several ADHD specific support groups exist as informational sources and to help families cope with challenges associated with dealing with ADHD.

A 2009 study found that children with ADHD move around a lot because it helps them stay alert enough to complete challenging tasks. The researcher advises that when they are doing homework, one should let them fidget, stand or chew gum since it may help them cope. Unless their behavior is destructive, severely limiting their activity could be counterproductive.[45]

Pharmacological treatment

Management with medication has been shown to be the most cost-effective, followed by behavioral treatment and combined treatment in a 14 month follow-up study.[127] However, a longer follow-up study of 3 years found that stimulant medication offered no benefits over behavioural therapy.[133] Stimulant medication or non-stimulant medication may be prescribed. A 2007 drug class review found that there are no good studies of comparative effectiveness between various drugs for ADHD and that there is a lack of quality evidence on their effects on overall academic performance and social behaviors.[134] The long term effects of ADHD medications in preschool children are unknown and are not recommended for pre-school children.[33] [135] There is very little data on the long-term adverse effects or benefits of stimulants for ADHD.[136]

Stimulant medication

Stimulants are the most commonly prescribed medications for ADHD. The most common stimulant medications are the chain subsitituted amphetamine methylphenidate (Ritalin, Metadate, Concerta), dextroamphetamine (Dexedrine), mixed amphetamine salts (Adderall),[137] [138] dextromethamphetamine (Desoxyn)[139] and lisdexamfetamine (Vyvanse).[140]

A meta analysis of clinical trials found that about 70% of children improve after being treated with stimulants in the short term but found that this conclusion may be biased due to the high number of low quality clinical trials in the literature. There have been no randomized placebo controlled clinical trials investigating the long term effectiveness of methylphenidate (Ritalin) beyond 4 weeks. Thus the long term effectiveness of methylphenidate has not been scientifically demonstrated. Serious concerns of publication bias regarding the use of methylphenidate for ADHD has also been noted.[141]

Higher rates of schizophrenia and bipolar disorder as well as increased severity of these disorders occur in individuals with a past history of stimulant use for ADHD in childhood.[142]

Both children with and without ADHD abuse stimulants, with ADHD individuals being at the highest risk of abusing or diverting their stimulant prescriptions. Between 16 and 29 percent of students who are prescribed stimulants report diverting their prescriptions. Between 5 and 9 percent of grade/primary and high school children and between 5 and 35 percent of college students have used nonprescribed stimulants. Most often their motivation is to concentrate, improve alertness, "get high," or to experiment.[143]

Stimulants used to treat ADHD raise the extracellular concentrations of the neurotransmitters dopamine and norepinephrine which causes an increase in neurotransmission. The therapeutic benefits are due to noradrenergic effects at the locus coeruleus and the prefrontal cortex and dopaminergic effects at the nucleus accumbens.[144]

One study found that children with ADHD actually *need* to move more to maintain the required level of alertness while performing tasks that challenge their working memory. Performing math problems mentally and remembering multi-step directions are examples of tasks that require working memory, which involves remembering and manipulating information for a short time. These findings may also explain why stimulant medications improve the behavior of most children with ADHD. Those medications improve the physiological arousal of children with ADHD, increasing their alertness.[45] Previous studies have shown that stimulant medications temporarily improve working memory abilities.

Although "under medical supervision, stimulant medications are considered safe",[113] [145] the use of stimulant medications for the treatment of ADHD has generated controversy because of undesirable side effects, uncertain long term effects[20] [136] [146] [147] [148] and social and ethical issues regarding their use and dispensation. The FDA has added black-box warnings to some ADHD medications,[149] [150] while the American Heart Association and the American Academy of Pediatrics feel that it is prudent to carefully assess children for heart conditions before treating them with stimulant medications.[151]

Antipsychotic medication

On the contrary to stimulant medication, atypical antipsychotic drug use is rising among ADHD children. Antipsychotics work by blocking dopamine whereas stimulants trigger its release, putting further stigma on the pharmacological treatment of ADHD. As a second-line approach to treatment in children who do not respond to stimulant medications, this class of drugs has not been well-studied or proven to work safely in children with the disorder. Weight gain, heart rhythm problems, diabetes and the possibility of irreversible movement disorders (tardive dyskinesia) are among the short and long-term adverse events associated with antipsychotic drugs.[152] [153]

Other non-stimulant medications

Atomoxetine (Strattera) is currently the only non-stimulant drug approved for the treatment of ADHD. Other medications which may be prescribed off-label include alpha-2A adrenergic receptor blockers such as guanfacine and clonidine, certain antidepressants such as tricyclic antidepressants, SNRIs or MAOIs.[154] [155] [156] [157] Another non-stimulant drug that has been used to treat ADHD is the analeptic drug modafinil. There have been double-blind randomised controlled trials that have demonstrated the efficacy and tolerability of modafinil,[158] [159] however there are risks of serious side effects such as skin reactions and modafinil is not recommended for use in children.[160]

Experimental/ Alternative treatments

Dietary supplements and specialized diets are sometimes used by people with ADHD with the intent to mitigate some or all of the symptoms. For example, Omega-3 supplementation (seal, fish or krill oil) may reduce ADHD symptoms for a subgroup of children and adolescents with ADHD "characterized by inattention and associated neurodevelopmental disorders."[161] Although vitamin or mineral supplements (micronutrients) may help children diagnosed with particular deficiencies, there is no evidence that they are helpful for all children with ADHD. Furthermore, *megadoses of vitamins, which can be toxic, must be avoided.*[162] In the United States, no dietary supplement has been approved for the treatment for ADHD by the FDA.[163] There is however a pilot study done which shows that phosphatidyl serine (PS) can help against ADHD.[164] [165]

EEG biofeedback is a treatment strategy used for children, adolescents and adults with ADHD.[166] The human brain emits electrical energy which is measured with electrodes on the brain. Biofeedback alerts the patient when beta waves are present. This theory believes that those with ADHD can train themselves to decrease ADHD symptoms. There is a distinct split in the scientific community about the effectiveness of the treatment. A number of studies indicate the scientific evidence has been increasing in recent years for the effectiveness of EEG biofeedback for the treatment of ADHD. According to a 2007 review, with effectiveness of the treatment was demonstrated to be equivalent to that of stimulant medication. The review noted, improvements are seen at the behavioral and neuropsychological level with the symptoms of inattention, hyperactivity and impulsivity showing significant decreases after treatment. There are no known side effects from EEG biofeedback therapy. There are methodological limitations and weaknesses in study designs however. In a 2005 review, Loo and Barkley stated that problems including lack of blinding such as placebo control and randomisation are significant limitations to the studies into EEG biofeedback and make definitive conclusions impossible to make.[167] As a result more robust clinical studies have been strongly recommended.[168] A German review in 2004 found that EEG biofeedback, also sometimes referred to as neurofeedback, is more effective than previously thought in treating attention deficiency, impulsivity and hyperactivity; short-term effects match those of stimulant treatment and a persistent normalization of EEG parameters is found which is not found after treatment with stimulants.[169] There are no known side effects from biofeedback therapy although research into biofeedback has been limited and further research has been recommended.[169] An American review the following year also emphasized the benefits of this method.[170] Similar findings were reported in a study by another German team in 2004.[171]

Aerobic fitness may improve cognitive functioning and neural organization related to executive control during pre-adolescent development, though more studies are needed in this area.[172] One study suggests that athletic performance in boys with ADHD may increase peer acceptance when accompanied by fewer negative behaviors.[173]

Art is thought by some to be an effective therapy for some of the symptoms of ADHD. Other sources, including some psychologists who have written on the subject, feel that cutting down on time spent on television, video games, or violent media can help some children. One study indicated a correlation between excessive TV time as a child with higher rates of ADHD symptoms.[174] Other therapies that have been effective for some have been ADHD coaching, positive changes in diet, such as low sugar, low additives, and no caffeine. Children who spend time outdoors in natural settings, such as parks, seem to display fewer symptoms of ADHD, which has been dubbed

"Green Therapy".[175]

Prognosis

Children diagnosed with ADHD have significant difficulties in adolescence, regardless of treatment.[176] In the United States, 37% of those with ADHD do not get a high school diploma even though many of them will receive special education services.[34] A 1995 briefing citing a 1994 book review says the combined outcomes of the expulsion and dropout rates indicate that almost half of all ADHD students never finish high school.[177] Also in the US, less than 5% of individuals with ADHD get a college degree[178] compared to 28% of the general population.[179] Those with ADHD as children are at increased risk of a number of adverse life outcomes once they become teenagers. These include a greater risk of auto crashes, injury and higher medical expenses, earlier sexual activity, and teen pregnancy.[180] Russell Barkley states that adult ADHD impairments affect "education, occupation, social relationships, sexual activities, dating and marriage, parenting and offspring psychological morbidity, crime and drug abuse, health and related lifestyles, financial management, or driving. ADHD can be found to produce diverse and serious impairments".[181] The proportion of children meeting the diagnostic criteria for ADHD drops by about 50% over three years after the diagnosis. This occurs regardless of the treatments used and also occurs in untreated children with ADHD.[121] [133] [147] ADHD persists into adulthood in about 30-50% of cases.[17] Those affected are likely to develop coping mechanisms as they mature, thus compensating for their previous ADHD.[19]

Epidemiology

ADHD's global prevalence is estimated at 3-5% in people under the age of 19. There is, however, both geographical and local variability among studies. Geographically, children in North America appear to have a higher rate of ADHD than children in Africa and the Middle East,[182] well published studies have found rates of ADHD as low as 2% and as high as 14% among school aged children.[36] The rates of diagnosis and treatment of ADHD are also much higher on the East Coast of the USA than on the West Coast.[183] The frequency of the diagnosis differs between male children (10%) and female children (4%) in the United States.[184] This difference between genders may reflect either a difference in susceptibility or that females with ADHD are less likely to be diagnosed than males.[185]

Rates of ADHD diagnosis and treatment have increased in both the UK and the USA since the 1970s. In the UK an estimated 0.5 per 1,000 children had ADHD in the 1970s, while 3 per 1,000 received ADHD medications in the late 1990s. In the USA in the 1970s 12 per 1,000 children had the diagnosis, while in the late 1990s 34 per 1,000 had the diagnosis and the numbers continue to increase.[33]

In the UK in 2003 a prevalence of 3.6% is reported in male children and less than 1% is reported in female children.[186]

As of 2009[187], eight percent of all Major League Baseball players have been diagnosed with ADHD, making the disease epidemic among this population. The increase coincided with the League's 2006 ban on stimulants (q.v. Major League Baseball drug policy).[188]

History

Hyperactivity has long been part of the human condition. Sir Alexander Crichton describes "mental restlessness" in his 1798 book.[189] [190] The terminology used to describe the symptoms of ADHD has gone through many changes over history including: "minimal brain damage", "minimal brain dysfunction", "learning/behavioral disabilities" and "hyperactivity". In the DSM-II (1968) it was the "Hyperkinetic Reaction of Childhood". In the DSM-III "ADD (Attention-Deficit Disorder) with or without hyperactivity" was introduced. In 1987 this was changed to ADHD in the DSM-III-R and subsequent editions.[191] The use of stimulants to treat ADHD was first described in 1937.[192]

Society and culture

The media have reported on many issues related to ADHD. In 2001 PBS's Frontline aired a one-hour program about the effects of the diagnosis and treatment of ADHD in minors, entitled "Medicating Kids."[193] The program included a selection of interviews with representatives of various points of view. In one segment, entitled Backlash, retired neurologist Fred Baughman and Peter Breggin whom PBS described as "outspoken critics who insist [ADHD is] a fraud perpetrated by the psychiatric and pharmaceutical industries on families anxious to understand their children's behavior"[194] were interviewed on the legitimacy of the disorder. Russell Barkley and Xavier Castellanos, then head of ADHD research at the National Institute of Mental Health (NIMH), defended the viability of the disorder. In the interview with Castellanos, he stated that little is scientifically understood.[195] Lawrence Diller was interviewed on the business of ADHD along with a representative from Shire Plc.

A number of notable individuals have given controversial opinions on ADHD. Scientologist Tom Cruise's interview with Matt Lauer was widely watched by the public. In this interview he spoke about postpartum depression and also referred to Ritalin and Adderall as being "street drugs" rather than as ADHD medication.[196] In England Baroness Susan Greenfield, a leading neuroscientist, spoke out publicly about the need for a wide-ranging inquiry in the House of Lords into the dramatic increase in the diagnosis of ADHD in the UK and possible causes[197] following a 2007 BBC Panorama programme which highlighted US research (The Multimodal Treatment Study of Children with ADHD by the University of Buffalo showing treatment results of 600) suggesting drugs are no better than other forms of therapy for ADHD in the long term.[198]

Controversies

ADHD and its diagnosis and treatment have been considered controversial since the 1970s.[25] [27] [199] The controversies have involved clinicians, teachers, policymakers, parents and the media. Opinions regarding ADHD range from not believing it exists at all to believing there are genetic and physiological bases for the condition as well as disagreement about the use of stimulant medications in treatment.[26] [27] [28] Most healthcare providers accept that ADHD is a genuine disorder with debate in the scientific community centering mainly around how it is diagnosed and treated.[29] [30] [31]

Others have included that it may stem from a misunderstanding of the diagnostic criteria and how they are utilized by clinicians,[13] :p.3 teachers, policymakers, parents and the media.[26] Debates center around: whether ADHD is a disability or whether it is merely a neurological description, the cause of the disorder, the changing of the diagnostic criteria, and the rapid increase in diagnosis of ADHD and the use of stimulants to treat the disorder.[200] Some do not believe it exists at all.[26] Long term possible side effects of stimulants and their usefulness are largely unknown because of a lack of long term studies.[201] Some research raises questions about the long term effectiveness and side effects of medications used to treat ADHD.[202]

In 1998, the US National Institutes of Health (NIH) released a consensus statement on the diagnosis and treatment of ADHD. The statement, while recognizing that stimulant treatment is controversial, supports the validity of the ADHD diagnosis and the efficacy of stimulant treatment. It found controversy only in the lack of sufficient data on long-term use of medications, and in the need for more research in many areas.[203]

The British Psychological Society said in a 1997 report that physicians and psychiatrists should not follow the American example of applying medical labels to such a wide variety of attention-related disorders: "The idea that children who don't attend or who don't sit still in school have a mental disorder is not entertained by most British clinicians."[204] [205]

However, several years later, in 2009, the British Psychological Society, in collaboration with the Royal College of Psychiatrists, released a set of guidelines for the diagnosis and treatment of ADHD.[206]

References

[1] http://apps.who.int/classifications/apps/icd/icd10online/?g

[2] http://www.icd9data.com/getICD9Code.ashx?icd9=314.00

[3] http://www.icd9data.com/getICD9Code.ashx?icd9=314.01

[4] http://www.ncbi.nlm.nih.gov/entrez/dispomim.cgi?id=143465

[5] http://www.diseasesdatabase.com/ddb6158.htm

[6] http://www.nlm.nih.gov/medlineplus/ency/article/001551.htm

[7] http://www.emedicine.com/med/topic3103.htm

[8] http://www.emedicine.com/ped/topic177.htm#

[9] http://www.nlm.nih.gov/cgi/mesh/2009/MB_cgi?field=uid&term=D001289

[10] NINDS Attention Deficit-Hyperactivity Disorder Information Page. (http://www.ninds.nih.gov/disorders/adhd/adhd.htm) National Institute of Neurological Disorders and Stroke (NINDS/NIH) February 9, 2007. Retrieved on 2007-08-13.

[11] Zwi M, Ramchandani P, Joughin C (October 2000). " Evidence and belief in ADHD (http://www.pubmedcentral.nih.gov/articlerender. fcgi?tool=pmcentrez&artid=1118810)". *BMJ* **321** (7267): 975–6. doi: 10.1136/bmj.321.7267.975 (http://dx.doi.org/10.1136/bmj.321. 7267.975). PMID 11039942 (http://www.ncbi.nlm.nih.gov/pubmed/11039942).

[12] Biederman J (1998). "Attention-deficit/hyperactivity disorder: a life-span perspective". *The Journal of Clinical Psychiatry* **59 Suppl 7**: 4–16. PMID 9680048 (http://www.ncbi.nlm.nih.gov/pubmed/9680048).

[13] Ramsay, J. Russell. *Cognitive Behavioral Therapy for Adult ADHD*. Routledge, 2007. ISBN 0415955017

[14] " NIMH • ADHD • Complete Publication (http://web.archive.org/web/20071018052052/http://www.nimh.nih.gov/health/ publications/adhd/complete-publication.shtml)". Archived from the original (http://www.nimh.nih.gov/health/publications/adhd/ complete-publication.shtml) on 2007-10-18. .

[15] Nair J, Ehimare U, Beitman BD, Nair SS, Lavin A (2006). "Clinical review: evidence-based diagnosis and treatment of ADHD in children". *Mo Med* **103** (6): 617–21. PMID 17256270 (http://www.ncbi.nlm.nih.gov/pubmed/17256270).

[16] Van Cleave J, Leslie LK (August 2008). "Approaching ADHD as a chronic condition: implications for long-term adherence". *Journal of psychosocial nursing and mental health services* **46** (8): 28–37. PMID 18777966 (http://www.ncbi.nlm.nih.gov/pubmed/18777966).

[17] Bálint S, Czobor P, Mészáros A, Simon V, Bitter I (2008). "[Neuropsychological impairments in adult attention deficit hyperactivity disorder: a literature review]" (in Hungarian). *Psychiatr Hung* **23** (5): 324–35. PMID 19129549 (http://www.ncbi.nlm.nih.gov/pubmed/ 19129549).

[18] Elia J, Ambrosini PJ, Rapoport JL (March 1999). " Treatment of attention-deficit-hyperactivity disorder (http://content.nejm.org/cgi/ content/extract/340/10/780)". *N. Engl. J. Med.* **340** (10): 780–8. doi: 10.1056/NEJM199903113401007 (http://dx.doi.org/10.1056/ NEJM199903113401007). PMID 10072414 (http://www.ncbi.nlm.nih.gov/pubmed/10072414). .

[19] Gentile, Julie (2004). " Adult ADHD: Diagnosis, Differential Diagnosis and Medication Management (http://www.psychiatrymmc.com/ displayArticle.cfm?articleID=article218)". *Psychiatry* **3** (8): 24–30. doi: 10.1383/psyt.3.8.24.43396 (http://dx.doi.org/10.1383/psyt.3.8. 24.43396). . Retrieved 2008-09-11.

[20] Stern HP, Stern TP (September 2002). "When children with attention-deficit/hyperactivity disorder become adults". *South. Med. J.* **95** (9): 985–91. PMID 12356139 (http://www.ncbi.nlm.nih.gov/pubmed/12356139).

[21] Barkley, Russell A. (2007). " ADHD in Adults: History, Diagnosis, and Impairments (http://www.continuingedcourses.net/active/ courses/course034.php)". ContinuingEdCourses.net. . Retrieved July 27, 2009.

[22] Dulcan M (October 1997). "Practice parameters for the assessment and treatment of children, adolescents and adults with attention-deficit/hyperactivity disorder. American Academy of Child and Adolescent Psychiatry". *J Am Acad Child Adolesc Psychiatry* **36** (10 Suppl): 85S–121S. PMID 9334567 (http://www.ncbi.nlm.nih.gov/pubmed/9334567).

[23] Singh I (December 2008). "Beyond polemics: science and ethics of ADHD". *Nat. Rev. Neurosci.* **9** (12): 957–64. doi: 10.1038/nrn2514 (http://dx.doi.org/10.1038/nrn2514). PMID 19020513 (http://www.ncbi.nlm.nih.gov/pubmed/19020513).

[24] Sciutto, M.J., Nolfi, C.J., & Bluhm, C. (2004). Effects of Child Gender and Symptom Type on Referrals for ADHD by Elementary School Teachers. *Journal of Emotional and Behavioral Disorders, 12*(4), 247-253.

[25] Parrillo, Vincent (2008). *Encyclopedia of Social Problems* (http://books.google.ca/books?id=mRGr_B4Y1CEC&pg=PA63& dq=percent+who+consider+ADHD+controversial&ei=kIEJScO6CY_-sQPYp62HAg). SAGE. p. 63. ISBN 9781412941655. . Retrieved 2009-05-02.

[26] " Treatment of Attention-Deficit/Hyperactivity Disorder (http://www.ahrq.gov/clinic/epcsums/adhdsum.htm)". US department of health and human services. December 1999. . Retrieved 2008-10-02.

[27] Mayes R, Bagwell C, Erkulwater J (2008). "ADHD and the rise in stimulant use among children". *Harv Rev Psychiatry* **16** (3): 151–66. doi: 10.1080/10673220802167782 (http://dx.doi.org/10.1080/10673220802167782). PMID 18569037 (http://www.ncbi.nlm.nih.gov/ pubmed/18569037).

[28] Cohen, Donald J.; Cicchetti, Dante (2006). *Developmental psychopathology*. Chichester: John Wiley & Sons. ISBN 0-471-23737-X.

[29] Sim MG, Hulse G, Khong E (August 2004). " When the child with ADHD grows up (http://www.racgp.org.au/afp/200408/ 20040803sim.pdf)" (PDF). *Aust Fam Physician* **33** (8): 615–8. PMID 15373378 (http://www.ncbi.nlm.nih.gov/pubmed/15373378). .

[30] Silver, Larry B. *Attention-deficit/hyperactivity disorder*. American Psychiatric Publishing, Inc.; 3 edition (September 2003) ISBN 1585621315; Online (http://books.google.com/books?id=gjojY1WoIOIC&pg=PA4&lpg=PP6&output=html) July 20, 2009

[31] Schonwald A, Lechner E (April 2006). "Attention deficit/hyperactivity disorder: complexities and controversies". *Curr. Opin. Pediatr.* **18** (2): 189–95. doi: 10.1097/01.mop.0000193302.70882.70 (http://dx.doi.org/10.1097/01.mop.0000193302.70882.70). PMID 16601502 (http://www.ncbi.nlm.nih.gov/pubmed/16601502).

[32] Goldman LS, Genel M, Bezman RJ, Slanetz PJ (April 1998). " Diagnosis and treatment of attention-deficit/hyperactivity disorder in children and adolescents. Council on Scientific Affairs, American Medical Association (http://jama.ama-assn.org/cgi/pmidlookup?view=long& pmid=9546570)". *JAMA* **279** (14): 1100–7. PMID 9546570 (http://www.ncbi.nlm.nih.gov/pubmed/9546570). .

[33] " CG72 Attention deficit hyperactivity disorder (ADHD): full guideline (http://www.nice.org.uk/nicemedia/pdf/CG72FullGuideline. pdf)" (PDF). NHS. 24 September 2008. . Retrieved 2008-10-08.

[34] " Attention-Deficit/Hyperactivity Disorder: Nature, Course, Outcomes, and Comorbidity. (http://www.continuingedcourses.net/active/ courses/course003.php)". *Barkley, Russell.* . Retrieved 2008-09-19.

[35] " Brain Matures A Few Years Late In ADHD, But Follows Normal Pattern (http://www.sciencedaily.com/releases/2007/11/ 071112172200.htm)". Sciencedaily.com. 2007-11-13. . Retrieved 2009-05-25.

[36] " LONI: Laboratory of Neuro Imaging (http://www.loni.ucla.edu/Research/Projects/ADHD.shtml#CurrentResearch)". . Retrieved 2008-09-19.

[37] Wiener, Jerry M., Editor (2003). *Textbook Of Child & Adolescent Psychiatry* (http://books.google.com/books?id=EIgGKcp0SpkC& dq=weiner+2003+"textbook+of+child+&+adolescent+psychiatry"&printsec=frontcover&source=in&hl=en& ei=L-n7SZPlFtiNsAaR2cjUBA&sa=X&oi=book_result&ct=result&resnum=11). Washington, DC: American Psychiatric Association. ISBN 1-58562-057-2. .

[38] DSM-IV-TR workgroup. The Diagnostic and Statistical Manual of Mental Disorders, Fourth Edition, Text Revision. Washington, DC: American Psychiatric Association.

[39] American Academy of Child Adolescent Psychiatry. "ADHD - A Guide for Families." June 27, 2009. http://www.aacap.org/cs/ adhd_a_guide_for_families/what_is_adhd

[40] Tom, Catherine M. (2005-01-15). *Recognizing and Treating ADHD in Adolescents and Adults* (http://web.archive.org/web/ 20080205232924/http://www.uspharmacist.com/index.asp?page=ce/10135/default.htm). uspharmacist.com. . Retrieved 2009-05-25.

[41] Gentile, Julie. *Adult ADHD: Diagnosis, Differential Diagnosis, and Medication Management* (http://www.psychiatrymmc.com/ displayArticle.cfm?articleID=article218). **3**. Psychiatrymmc.com. . Retrieved 2009-05-25.

[42] Kubose, Shauna. *ADHD in Adults: Are the Current Diagnostic Criteria Adequate?* (http://www.neuropsychiatryreviews.com/feb00/ npr_feb00_ADHD.html). **1**. Neuropsychiatryreviews.com. . Retrieved 2009-05-25.

[43] "Attention Deficit Hyperactivity Disorder (ADHD)." Health & Outreach. Publications. http://www.nimh.nih.gov/health/publications/ attention-deficit-hyperactivity-disorder/complete-index.shtml July 15, 2009

[44] Brewis, Alexandra; Schmidt, Karen L.; Meyer, Mary (2000-12). "ADHD-Type Behavior and Harmful Dysfunction in Childhood: A Cross-Cultural Model". *American Anthropologist* **102** (4): 826. doi: 10.1525/aa.2000.102.4.823 (http://dx.doi.org/10.1525/aa.2000.102. 4.823).

[45] "University of Central Florida Study: Hyperactivity Enables Children With ADHD to Stay Alert". Ascribe Newswire: Health, 3/9/2009.

[46] Brunsvold GL, Oepen G (2008). " Comorbid Depression in ADHD: Children and Adolescents (http://www.psychiatrictimes.com/adhd/ article/10168/1286863)". *Psychiatric Times* **25** (10). .

[47] " Evaluation and diagnosis of attention deficit hyperactivity disorder in children (http://www.uptodate.com/online/content/topic. do?topicKey=behavior/8293#5)" (Subscription required). Uptodate. December 5, 2007. . Retrieved 2008-09-12.

[48] Bauermeister, J., Shrout, P., Chávez, L., Rubio-Stipec, M., Ramírez, R., Padilla, L., et al. (2007, August). ADHD and gender: are risks and sequela of ADHD the same for boys and girls?. Journal of Child Psychology & Psychiatry, 48(8), 831-839. Retrieved February 17, 2009, doi:10.1111/j.1469-7610.2007.01750.x

[49] Bauermeister, J., Shrout, P., Chávez, L., Rubio-Stipec, M., Ramírez, R., Padilla, L., et al. (2007, August). ADHD and gender: are risks and sequela of ADHD the same for boys and girls?. Journal of Child Psychology & Psychiatry, 48(8), 831-839.

[50] Bailly, Lionel (2005). " Stimulant medication for the treatment of attention-deficit hyperactivity disorder: evidence-b(i)ased practice? (http:/ /pb.rcpsych.org/cgi/content/full/29/8/284)" (Full text). *Psychiatric Bulletin* (The Royal College of Psychiatrists) **29** (8): 284–287. doi: 10.1192/pb.29.8.284 (http://dx.doi.org/10.1192/pb.29.8.284). .

[51] Barkley, Russel A.. " Attention-Deficit/Hyperactivity Disorder: Nature, Course, Outcomes, and Comorbidity (http://www. continuingedcourses.net/active/courses/course003.php)". . Retrieved 2006-06-26.

[52] Volkow, ND; Wang, GJ; Kollins, SH; Wigal, TL; Newcorn, JH; Telang, F; Fowler, JS; Zhu, W *et al.* (2009). "Evaluating Dopamine Reward Pathway in ADHD". *JAMA* **302** (10): 1084–1091. doi: 10.1001/jama.2009.1308 (http://dx.doi.org/10.1001/jama.2009.1308). PMID 19738093 (http://www.ncbi.nlm.nih.gov/pubmed/19738093).

[53] Roman T, Rohde LA, Hutz MH. (2004). "Polymorphisms of the dopamine transporter gene: influence on response to methylphenidate in attention deficit-hyperactivity disorder." *American Journal of Pharmacogenomics* 4(2):83–92 PMID 15059031

[54] Swanson JM, Flodman P, Kennedy J, et al. "Dopamine Genes and ADHD." *Neurosci Biobehav Rev.* 2000 Jan;24(1):21–5. PMID 10654656

[55] Smith KM, Daly M, Fischer M, et al. "Association of the dopamine beta hydroxylase gene with attention deficit hyperactivity disorder: genetic analysis of the Milwaukee longitudinal study." *Am J Med Genet B Neuropsychiatr Genet.* 2003 May 15;119(1):77–85. PMID 12707943

[56] Acosta, MT; Arcos-Burgos, M; Muenke, M (2004). "Attention deficit/hyperactivity disorder (ADHD): Complex phenotype, simple genotype?". *Genetics in Medicine* **6** (1): 1–15. doi: 10.1097/01.GIM.0000110413.07490.0B (http://dx.doi.org/10.1097/01.GIM.

0000110413.07490.0B). PMID 14726804 (http://www.ncbi.nlm.nih.gov/pubmed/14726804).

[57] Arcos-Burgos M, Acosta MT (June 2007). " Tuning major gene variants conditioning human behavior: the anachronism of ADHD (http://linkinghub.elsevier.com/retrieve/pii/S0959-437X(07)00076-7)". *Curr. Opin. Genet. Dev.* **17** (3): 234–8. doi: 10.1016/j.gde.2007.04.011 (http://dx.doi.org/10.1016/j.gde.2007.04.011). PMID 17467976 (http://www.ncbi.nlm.nih.gov/pubmed/17467976). .

[58] Hartmann, Thom (2003). *The Edison gene: ADHD and the gift of the hunter child* (http://books.google.ca/books?id=L0l5EaHppyoC&dq=hunter+vs+farmer+The+Edison+Gene:+ADHD+and+the+Gift+of+the+Hunter+Child&lr=&source=gbs_summary_s&cad=0). Rochester, Vt: Park Street Press. ISBN 0-89281-128-5. .

[59] Williams J, Taylor E (June 2006). " The evolution of hyperactivity, impulsivity and cognitive diversity (http://www.pubmedcentral.nih.gov/articlerender.fcgi?tool=pmcentrez&artid=1578754)". *J R Soc Interface* **3** (8): 399–413. doi: 10.1098/rsif.2005.0102 (http://dx.doi.org/10.1098/rsif.2005.0102). PMID 16849269 (http://www.ncbi.nlm.nih.gov/pubmed/16849269).

[60] Levy et al., 1997

[61] Nigg, 2006

[62] Sherman, Silberg et al., 1996

[63] Sherman DK, Iacono WG, McGue MK (June 1997). "Attention-deficit hyperactivity disorder dimensions: a twin study of inattention and impulsivity-hyperactivity". *Journal of the American Academy of Child and Adolescent Psychiatry* **36** (6): 745–53. doi: 10.1097/00004583-199706000-00010 (http://dx.doi.org/10.1097/00004583-199706000-00010). PMID 9183128 (http://www.ncbi.nlm.nih.gov/pubmed/9183128).

[64] Braun JM, Kahn RS, Froehlich T, Auinger P, Lanphear BP (2006). " Exposures to environmental toxicants and attention deficit hyperactivity disorder in U.S. children (http://www.pubmedcentral.nih.gov/articlerender.fcgi?tool=pmcentrez&artid=1764142)". *Environ. Health Perspect.* **114** (12): 1904–9. doi: 10.1289/ehp.10274 (http://dx.doi.org/10.1289/ehp.10274). PMID 17185283 (http://www.ncbi.nlm.nih.gov/pubmed/17185283).

[65] " Bad behaviour 'linked to smoking' (http://news.bbc.co.uk/1/hi/health/4727197.stm)". BBC. 31 July 2005. . Retrieved 2008-12-30.

[66] " Ability To Quit Smoking May Depend On ADHD Symptoms, Researchers Find (http://www.sciencedaily.com/releases/2008/11/081121125602.htm)". Science Daily. 24 November 2008. . Retrieved 2008-12-30.

[67] " Prenatal Smoking Increases ADHD Risk In Some Children (http://www.sciencedaily.com/releases/2007/04/070410190421.htm)". Science Daily. 11 April 2007. . Retrieved 2008-12-30.

[68] " ADHD 'linked to premature birth' (http://news.bbc.co.uk/1/hi/health/5042308.stm)". BBC. 4 June 2006. . Retrieved 2008-12-30.

[69] Keenan HT, Hall GC, Marshall SW (2008). " Early head injury and attention deficit hyperactivity disorder: retrospective cohort study; (http://bmj.com/cgi/pmidlookup?view=long&pmid=18988644)". *BMJ* **337**: a1984. doi: 10.1136/bmj.a1984 (http://dx.doi.org/10.1136/bmj.a1984). PMID 18988644 (http://www.ncbi.nlm.nih.gov/pubmed/18988644). PMC 2590885 (http://www.pubmedcentral.nih.gov/articlerender.fcgi?tool=pmcentrez&artid=2590885). .

[70] " Mental Health: A report of the surgeon general (http://www.surgeongeneral.gov/library/mentalhealth/chapter3/sec4.html)". 1999. . Retrieved 2008-09-15.

[71] McCann D, Barrett A, Cooper A (November 2007). "Food additives and hyperactive behaviour in 3-year-old and 8/9-year-old children in the community: a randomised, double-blinded, placebo-controlled trial". *Lancet* **370** (9598): 1560–7. doi: 10.1016/S0140-6736(07)61306-3 (http://dx.doi.org/10.1016/S0140-6736(07)61306-3). PMID 17825405 (http://www.ncbi.nlm.nih.gov/pubmed/17825405).

[72] U.S. Food and Drug Administration (http://www.fda.gov/RegulatoryInformation/Legislation/FederalFoodDrugandCosmeticActFDCAct/default.htm)

[73] U.S. Food and Drug Administration (http://www.fda.gov/RegulatoryInformation/Legislation/FederalFoodDrugandCosmeticActFDCAct/FDCActChapterVIIGeneralAuthority/ucm109535.htm)

[74] What Keeps Children in Foster Care from Succeeding in School. (http://web.archive.org/web/20080306234634/http://www.vera.org/publication_pdf/169_280.pdf)PDF (661 KB)

[75] Adam James (2004) *Clinical psychology publishes critique of ADHD diagnosis and use of medication on children* (http://www.psychminded.co.uk/news/news2004/august04/Clinical psychology publishes critique of ADHD diagnosis and use of medication on children.htm) published on Psychminded.co.uk Psychminded Ltd

[76] Cuffe, S.P.; McCullough, Elizabeth L.; Pumariega, Andres J. (September 1994). " Comorbidity of attention Deficit Hyperactivity Disorder and Post-Traumatic Stress Disorder (http://www.springerlink.com/content/l24j735448007435/)". *Journal of Child and Family Studies* **3** (3): 327–336. doi: 10.1007/BF02234689 (http://dx.doi.org/10.1007/BF02234689). .

[77] " Sensory integration disorder (http://www.healthatoz.com/healthatoz/Atoz/common/standard/transform.jsp?requestURI=/healthatoz/Atoz/ency/sensory_integration_disorder.jsp)". healthatoz.com. 2006-08-14. . Retrieved 2008-12-30.

[78] Rethinking ADHD (http://www.palgrave.com/newsearch/title.aspx?PID=277194)

[79] Bailey, Eileen (2007-11-23). " ADHD and Creativity (http://www.healthcentral.com/adhd/c/1443/16796/adhd-creativity)". Healthcentral.com. . Retrieved 2009-05-25.

[80] Susan Smalley (2008). " Reframing ADHD in the Genomic Era (http://www.psychiatrictimes.com/adhd/article/10168/1163208)". *Psychiatric Times* **25** (7). .

[81] Parens E, Johnston J (2009). " Facts, values, and Attention-Deficit Hyperactivity Disorder (ADHD): an update on the controversies (http://www.pubmedcentral.nih.gov/articlerender.fcgi?tool=pmcentrez&artid=2637252)". *Child Adolesc Psychiatry Ment Health* **3** (1): 1. doi: 10.1186/1753-2000-3-1 (http://dx.doi.org/10.1186/1753-2000-3-1). PMID 19152690 (http://www.ncbi.nlm.nih.gov/pubmed/19152690).

[82] Chriss, James J. (2007). *Social control: an introduction*. Cambridge, UK: Polity. p. 230. ISBN 0-7456-3858-9.

[83] Szasz, Thomas Stephen (2001). *Pharmacracy: medicine and politics in America*. New York: Praeger. p. 212. ISBN 0-275-97196-1.

[84] " Attention Deficit Hyperactivity Disorder is a neurologically based disorder (http://www.incrediblehorizons.com/Understanding Add. htm)". Incrediblehorizons.com. . Retrieved 2009-05-25.

[85] " ADHD (http://www.sci.csuhayward.edu/~dsandberg/CHLDPATHLECTS/ChldPathLect05ADHD.htm)". Sci.csuhayward.edu. . Retrieved 2009-05-25.

[86] Sikström S, Söderlund G (October 2007). " Stimulus-dependent dopamine release in attention-deficit/hyperactivity disorder (http://content. apa.org/journals/rev/114/4/1047)". *Psychol Rev* **114** (4): 1047–75. doi: 10.1037/0033-295X.114.4.1047 (http://dx.doi.org/10.1037/ 0033-295X.114.4.1047). PMID 17907872 (http://www.ncbi.nlm.nih.gov/pubmed/17907872). .

[87] " Evaluation and diagnosis of attention deficit hyperactivity disorder in children (http://www.uptodate.com/online/content/topic. do?topicKey=behavior/8293&selectedTitle=4~150&source=search_result)". December 5, 2007. . Retrieved 2008-09-15.

[88] Krain, AL; Castellanos, FX (2006). "Brain development and ADHD". *Clinical Psychology Review* **26** (4): 433–444. doi: 10.1016/j.cpr.2006.01.005 (http://dx.doi.org/10.1016/j.cpr.2006.01.005). PMID 16480802 (http://www.ncbi.nlm.nih.gov/pubmed/ 16480802).

[89] " MerckMedicus Modules: ADHD - Pathophysiology (http://www.merckmedicus.com/pp/us/hcp/diseasemodules/adhd/ pathophysiology.jsp)". .

[90] Bush G, Valera EM, Seidman LJ (June 2005). "Functional neuroimaging of attention-deficit/hyperactivity disorder: a review and suggested future directions". *Biological Psychiatry* **57** (11): 1273–84. doi: 10.1016/j.biopsych.2005.01.034 (http://dx.doi.org/10.1016/j.biopsych. 2005.01.034). PMID 15949999 (http://www.ncbi.nlm.nih.gov/pubmed/15949999).

[91] Brain Matures a Few Years Late in ADHD, But Follows Normal Pattern (http://www.nimh.nih.gov/science-news/2007/ brain-matures-a-few-years-late-in-adhd-but-follows-normal-pattern.shtml) NIMH Press Release, November 12, 2007

[92] Joshi SV; Adam, H. M. (February 2002). "ADHD, growth deficits, and relationships to psychostimulant use". *Pediatrics in Review* **23** (2): 67–8; discussion 67–8. doi: 10.1542/pir.23-2-67 (http://dx.doi.org/10.1542/pir.23-2-67). PMID 11826259 (http://www.ncbi.nlm.nih. gov/pubmed/11826259).

[93] Gene Predicts Better Outcome as Cortex Normalizes in Teens with ADHD (http://www.nimh.nih.gov/science-news/2007/ gene-predicts-better-outcome-as-cortex-normalizes-in-teens-with-adhd.shtml) NIMH Press Release, August 6, 2007

[94] Lou HC, Andresen J, Steinberg B, McLaughlin T, Friberg L. "The striatum in a putative cerebral network activated by verbal awareness in normals and in ADHD children." *Eur J Neurol*. 1998 Jan;5(1):67–74. PMID 10210814

[95] Dougherty DD, Bonab AA, Spencer TJ, Madras BK, Fischman AJ (1999). "Dopamine transporter density in patients with attention deficit hyperactivity disorder". *Lancet* **354** (9196): 2132–33. doi: 10.1016/S0140-6736(99)04030-1 (http://dx.doi.org/10.1016/ S0140-6736(99)04030-1). PMID 10609822 (http://www.ncbi.nlm.nih.gov/pubmed/10609822).

[96] Dresel SH, Kung MP, Plössl K, Meegalla SK, Kung HF (1998). "Pharmacological effects of dopaminergic drugs on in vivo binding of [99mTc]TRODAT-1 to the central dopamine transporters in rats". *European journal of nuclear medicine* **25** (1): 31–9. PMID 9396872 (http:// www.ncbi.nlm.nih.gov/pubmed/9396872).

[97] Coccaro EF, Hirsch SL, Stein MA (2007). "Plasma homovanillic acid correlates inversely with history of learning problems in healthy volunteer and personality disordered subjects". *Psychiatry research* **149** (1–3): 297–302. doi: 10.1016/j.psychres.2006.05.009 (http://dx.doi. org/10.1016/j.psychres.2006.05.009). PMID 17113158 (http://www.ncbi.nlm.nih.gov/pubmed/17113158).

[98] Zametkin AJ, Nordahl TE, Gross M (November 1990). "Cerebral glucose metabolism in adults with hyperactivity of childhood onset". *N. Engl. J. Med.* **323** (20): 1361–6. PMID 2233902 (http://www.ncbi.nlm.nih.gov/pubmed/2233902).

[99] Matochik JA, Liebenauer LL, King AC, Szymanski HV, Cohen RM, Zametkin AJ (May 1994). " Cerebral glucose metabolism in adults with attention deficit hyperactivity disorder after chronic stimulant treatment (http://ajp.psychiatryonline.org/cgi/pmidlookup?view=long& pmid=8166305)". *Am J Psychiatry* **151** (5): 658–64. PMID 8166305 (http://www.ncbi.nlm.nih.gov/pubmed/8166305). .

[100] Zametkin AJ, Liebenauer LL, Fitzgerald GA (May 1993). "Brain metabolism in teenagers with attention-deficit hyperactivity disorder". *Arch. Gen. Psychiatry* **50** (5): 333–40. PMID 8489322 (http://www.ncbi.nlm.nih.gov/pubmed/8489322).

[101] Ernst M, Cohen RM, Liebenauer LL, Jons PH, Zametkin AJ (October 1997). "Cerebral glucose metabolism in adolescent girls with attention-deficit/hyperactivity disorder". *J Am Acad Child Adolesc Psychiatry* **36** (10): 1399–406. doi: 10.1097/00004583-199710000-00022 (http://dx.doi.org/10.1097/00004583-199710000-00022). PMID 9334553 (http://www.ncbi.nlm.nih.gov/pubmed/9334553).

[102] Armstrong, Thomas (1999). MAVM2K6SdAfcSf0nGYQ&hl=en&sa=X&oi=book_result&resnum=1&ct=result#PPA3,M1 *Add/Adhd Alternatives in the Classroom* (http://books.google.ca/books?id=EzXt100I4A8C&pg=PA3&lpg=PA3&dq=National+Institute+of+ Mental+Health+ADHD+PET+scan&source=web&ots=GlP-TIeiqN&sig=JADzxFyez-). ASCD. pp. 3–5. ISBN 9780871203595. MAVM2K6SdAfcSf0nGYQ&hl=en&sa=X&oi=book_result&resnum=1&ct=result#PPA3,M1. Retrieved 2009-05-02.

[103] Ernst M, Liebenauer LL, King AC, Fitzgerald GA, Cohen RM, Zametkin AJ (1994). "Reduced brain metabolism in hyperactive girls". *J Am Acad Child Adolesc Psychiatry* **33** (6): 858–68. doi: 10.1097/00004583-199407000-00012 (http://dx.doi.org/10.1097/ 00004583-199407000-00012). PMID 8083143 (http://www.ncbi.nlm.nih.gov/pubmed/8083143).

[104] Díaz-Heijtz R, Mulas F, Forssberg H (February 2006). " [Alterations in the pattern of dopaminergic markers in attention-deficit/hyperactivity disorder]]" (in Spanish). *Revista De Neurologia* **42 Suppl 2**: S19–23. PMID [http://www.ncbi.nlm.nih.gov/pubmed/16555214 16555214 (http://www.revneurol.com/LinkOut/formMedLine.asp?Refer=2005798& Revista=RevNeurol). .

[105] Philip Shaw, MD; Jason Lerch, PhD; Deanna Greenstein, PhD; Wendy Sharp, MSW; Liv Clasen, PhD; Alan Evans, PhD; Jay Giedd, MD; F. Xavier Castellanos, MD *et al.* (2006). "Longitudinal Mapping of Cortical Thickness and Clinical Outcome in Children and Adolescents With Attention-Deficit/Hyperactivity Disorder". *Arch Gen Psychiatry* 5 (63): 540–549. doi: 10.1001/archpsyc.63.5.540 (http://dx.doi.org/10.1001/archpsyc.63.5.540). PMID 16651511 (http://www.ncbi.nlm.nih.gov/pubmed/16651511).

[106] David Cohen (2004). " An Update on ADHD Neuroimaging Research (http://psychrights.org/research/Digest/NLPs/neruoimagingupdate.pdf)" (PDF). *The Journal of Mind and Behavior* (The Institute of Mind and Behavior, Inc) 25 (2): 161–166. ISSN 0271–0137 (http://worldcat.org/issn/0271-0137). . Retrieved 2009-05-25.

[107] David Cohen (2003). "Broken brains or flawed studies? A critical review of ADHD neuroimaging studies". *The Journal of Mind and Behavior* 24: 29–56.

[108] Joughin C, Ramchandani P, Zwi M (May 2003). " Attention-deficit/hyperactivity disorder (http://www.aafp.org/afp/20030501/british.html)". *Am Fam Physician* 67 (9): 1969–70. PMID 12751659 (http://www.ncbi.nlm.nih.gov/pubmed/12751659). . Retrieved 2009-05-02.

[109] Moffitt TE, Melchior M (June 2007). " Why does the worldwide prevalence of childhood attention deficit hyperactivity disorder matter? (http://www.pubmedcentral.nih.gov/articlerender.fcgi?tool=pmcentrez&artid=1994964)". *The American journal of psychiatry* 164 (6): 856–8. doi: 10.1176/appi.ajp.164.6.856 (http://dx.doi.org/10.1176/appi.ajp.164.6.856). PMID 17541041 (http://www.ncbi.nlm.nih.gov/pubmed/17541041).

[110] PMID 16585277

[111] " PsychiatryOnline (http://www.psychiatryonline.com/content.aspx?aID=7721)". .

[112] ICD Version 2006: F91. (http://www.who.int/classifications/apps/icd/icd10online/) World Health Organization. Retrieved on December 11, 2006.

[113] American Academy of Pediatrics. Subcommittee on Attention-Deficit/Hyperactivity Disorder and Committee on Quality Improvement. (October 2001). "Clinical practice guideline: treatment of the school-aged child with attention-deficit/hyperactivity disorder". *Pediatrics* 108 (4): 1033–44. doi: 10.1542/peds.108.4.1033 (http://dx.doi.org/10.1542/peds.108.4.1033). PMID 11581465 (http://www.ncbi.nlm.nih.gov/pubmed/11581465).

[114] Medscape.com (http://medoffice.medscape.com/viewarticle/530193_2) (subscription required)

[115] Pliszka S (2000). "Patterns of psychiatric comorbidity with attention-deficit/hyperactivity disorder". *Child Adolesc Psychiatr Clin N Am* 9 (3): 525–40, vii. PMID 10944655 (http://www.ncbi.nlm.nih.gov/pubmed/10944655).

[116] Lamminmäky T *(1995). "Attention deficit hyperactivity disorder subtypes: Are there differences in academic problems?".* Dev neuropsychology *(11): 297–310.*

[117] Foster EM, Jensen PS, Schlander M (February 2007). " Treatment for ADHD: is more complex treatment cost-effective for more complex cases? (http://www.pubmedcentral.nih.gov/articlerender.fcgi?tool=pmcentrez&artid=1955245)". *Health Services Research* 42 (1 Pt 1): 165–82. doi: 10.1111/j.1475-6773.2006.00599.x (http://dx.doi.org/10.1111/j.1475-6773.2006.00599.x). PMID 17355587 (http://www.ncbi.nlm.nih.gov/pubmed/17355587).

[118] Lynskey MT, Hall W (June 2001). "Attention deficit hyperactivity disorder and substance use disorders: Is there a causal link?". *Addiction* 96 (6): 815–22. doi: 10.1080/09652140020050988 (http://dx.doi.org/10.1080/09652140020050988). PMID 11399213 (http://www.ncbi.nlm.nih.gov/pubmed/11399213).

[119] Tan M, Appleton R (January 2005). " Attention deficit and hyperactivity disorder, methylphenidate, and epilepsy (http://www.pubmedcentral.nih.gov/articlerender.fcgi?tool=pmcentrez&artid=1720074)". *Archives of Disease in Childhood* 90 (1): 57–9. doi: 10.1136/adc.2003.048504 (http://dx.doi.org/10.1136/adc.2003.048504). PMID 15613514 (http://www.ncbi.nlm.nih.gov/pubmed/15613514).

[120] Aldenkamp AP, Arzimanoglou A, Reijs R, Van Mil S (December 2006). " Optimizing therapy of seizures in children and adolescents with ADHD (http://www.neurology.org/cgi/pmidlookup?view=long&pmid=17190923)". *Neurology* 67 (12 Suppl 4): S49–51. PMID 17190923 (http://www.ncbi.nlm.nih.gov/pubmed/17190923). .

[121] Smucker WD, Hedayat M (September 2001). " Evaluation and treatment of ADHD (http://www.aafp.org/afp/20010901/817.html)". *American Family Physician* 64 (5): 817–29. PMID 11563573 (http://www.ncbi.nlm.nih.gov/pubmed/11563573). .

[122] Owens JA (August 2005). "The ADHD and sleep conundrum: a review". *Journal of Developmental and Behavioral Pediatrics* 26 (4): 312–22. doi: 10.1097/00004703-200508000-00011 (http://dx.doi.org/10.1097/00004703-200508000-00011). PMID 16100507 (http://www.ncbi.nlm.nih.gov/pubmed/16100507).

[123] Owens JA (October 2008). "Sleep disorders and attention-deficit/hyperactivity disorder". *Current Psychiatry Reports* 10 (5): 439–44. doi: 10.1007/s11920-008-0070-x (http://dx.doi.org/10.1007/s11920-008-0070-x). PMID 18803919 (http://www.ncbi.nlm.nih.gov/pubmed/18803919).

[124] Golan N, Shahar E, Ravid S, Pillar G (March 2004). "Sleep disorders and daytime sleepiness in children with attention-deficit/hyperactive disorder". *Sleep* 27 (2): 261–6. PMID 15124720 (http://www.ncbi.nlm.nih.gov/pubmed/15124720).

[125] Walters AS, Silvestri R, Zucconi M, Chandrashekariah R, Konofal E (December 2008). " Review of the possible relationship and hypothetical links between attention deficit hyperactivity disorder (ADHD) and the simple sleep related movement disorders, parasomnias, hypersomnias, and circadian rhythm disorders (http://www.websciences.org/cftemplate/NAPS/archives/indiv.cfm?ID=20083790)". *Journal of Clinical Sleep Medicine* 4 (6): 591–600. PMID 19110891 (http://www.ncbi.nlm.nih.gov/pubmed/19110891). PMC 2603539 (http://www.pubmedcentral.nih.gov/articlerender.fcgi?tool=pmcentrez&artid=2603539). .

[126] Van der Heijden, K.B.; Smits, M.G., Van Someren, E.J., Gunning, W.B. (2005). " Idiopathic chronic sleep onset insomnia in attention-deficit/hyperactivity disorder: a circadian rhythm sleep disorder (http://www.ncbi.nlm.nih.gov/sites/entrez?Db=pubmed&

Cmd=ShowDetailView&TermToSearch=16076654&ordinalpos=4&itool=EntrezSystem2.PEntrez.Pubmed.Pubmed_ResultsPanel. Pubmed_RVDocSum)" (Free abstract.). *Chronobiol Int.* **22** (3): 559–70. PMID 16076654 (http://www.ncbi.nlm.nih.gov/pubmed/ 16076654). . Retrieved 2009-11-13.

[127] Jensen PS, Garcia JA, Glied S (September 2005). "Cost-effectiveness of ADHD treatments: findings from the multimodal treatment study of children with ADHD". *The American Journal of Psychiatry* **162** (9): 1628–36. doi: 10.1176/appi.ajp.162.9.1628 (http://dx.doi.org/10. 1176/appi.ajp.162.9.1628). PMID 16135621 (http://www.ncbi.nlm.nih.gov/pubmed/16135621).

[128] Yamada A, Takeuchi H, Miki H, Touge T, Deguchi K (July 1990). "[Acute transverse myelitis associated with ECHO-25 virus infection]" (in Japanese). *Rinshō Shinkeigaku* **30** (7): 784–6. PMID 2242635 (http://www.ncbi.nlm.nih.gov/pubmed/2242635).

[129] Fabiano GA, Pelham WE, Coles EK, Gnagy EM, Chronis-Tuscano A, O'Connor BC (March 2009). "A meta-analysis of behavioral treatments for attention-deficit/hyperactivity disorder". *Clinical Psychology Review* **29** (2): 129–40. doi: 10.1016/j.cpr.2008.11.001 (http:// dx.doi.org/10.1016/j.cpr.2008.11.001). PMID 19131150 (http://www.ncbi.nlm.nih.gov/pubmed/19131150).

[130] Pliszka S; AACAP Work Group on Quality Issues (July 2007). "Practice parameter for the assessment and treatment of children and adolescents with attention-deficit/hyperactivity disorder". *Journal of the American Academy of Child and Adolescent Psychiatry* **46** (7): 894–921. doi: 10.1097/chi.0b013e318054e724 (http://dx.doi.org/10.1097/chi.0b013e318054e724). PMID 17581453 (http://www.ncbi. nlm.nih.gov/pubmed/17581453).

[131] " Family therapy for attention-deficit disorder or attention-deficit/hyperactivity disorder in children and adolescents (http://www. cochrane.org/reviews/en/ab005042.html)". The Cochrane Collaboration. April 20, 2005. . Retrieved 2008-09-19.

[132] Wymbs BT, Pelham WE, Molina BS, Gnagy EM, Wilson TK, Greenhouse JB (October 2008). " Rate and predictors of divorce among parents of youths with ADHD (http://www.pubmedcentral.nih.gov/articlerender.fcgi?tool=pmcentrez&artid=2631569)". *Journal of Consulting and Clinical Psychology* **76** (5): 735–44. doi: 10.1037/a0012719 (http://dx.doi.org/10.1037/a0012719). PMID 18837591 (http://www.ncbi.nlm.nih.gov/pubmed/18837591).

[133] Jensen PS, Arnold LE, Swanson JM (August 2007). "3-year follow-up of the NIMH MTA study". *Journal of the American Academy of Child and Adolescent Psychiatry* **46** (8): 989–1002. doi: 10.1097/CHI.0b013e3180686d48 (http://dx.doi.org/10.1097/CHI. 0b013e3180686d48). PMID 17667478 (http://www.ncbi.nlm.nih.gov/pubmed/17667478).

[134] McDonagh MS, Peterson K, Dana T, Thakurta S. (2007). Drug Class Review on Pharmacologic Treatments for ADHD. Results (http:// www.ncbi.nlm.nih.gov/books/bv.fcgi?rid=adhd.chapter.53).

[135] Greenhill LL, Posner K, Vaughan BS, Kratochvil CJ (April 2008). "Attention deficit hyperactivity disorder in preschool children". *Child and Adolescent Psychiatric Clinics of North America* **17** (2): 347–66, ix. doi: 10.1016/j.chc.2007.11.004 (http://dx.doi.org/10.1016/j.chc. 2007.11.004). PMID 18295150 (http://www.ncbi.nlm.nih.gov/pubmed/18295150).

[136] King S, Griffin S, Hodges Z (July 2006). " A systematic review and economic model of the effectiveness and cost-effectiveness of methylphenidate, dexamfetamine and atomoxetine for the treatment of attention deficit hyperactivity disorder in children and adolescents (http://www.hta.ac.uk/execsumm/summ1023.htm)". *Health Technology Assessment* **10** (23): iii–iv, xiii–146. PMID 16796929 (http:// www.ncbi.nlm.nih.gov/pubmed/16796929). .

[137] Stephen V. Faraone, P. (2003, September 18). Retrieved from Medscape Today: Medscape.com (http://www.medscape.com/viewarticle/ 461543)

[138] Sulzer D, Sonders MS, Poulsen NW, Galli A (April 2005). "Mechanisms of neurotransmitter release by amphetamines: a review". *Progress in Neurobiology* **75** (6): 406–33. doi: 10.1016/j.pneurobio.2005.04.003 (http://dx.doi.org/10.1016/j.pneurobio.2005.04.003). PMID 15955613 (http://www.ncbi.nlm.nih.gov/pubmed/15955613).

[139] National Toxicology, Program (July 2005). "NTP-CERHR monograph on the potential human reproductive and developmental effects of amphetamines". *Ntp Cerhr Mon* (16): vii–III1. PMID 16130031 (http://www.ncbi.nlm.nih.gov/pubmed/16130031).

[140] Howland RH (August 2008). "Lisdexamfetamine: a prodrug stimulant for ADHD". *Journal of Psychosocial Nursing and Mental Health Services* **46** (8): 19–22. PMID 18777964 (http://www.ncbi.nlm.nih.gov/pubmed/18777964).

[141] Schachter HM, Pham B, King J, Langford S, Moher D (November 2001). " How efficacious and safe is short-acting methylphenidate for the treatment of attention-deficit disorder in children and adolescents? A meta-analysis (http://www.cmaj.ca/cgi/pmidlookup?view=long& pmid=11762571)". *CMAJ* **165** (11): 1475–88. PMID 11762571 (http://www.ncbi.nlm.nih.gov/pubmed/11762571). PMC 81663 (http:// www.pubmedcentral.nih.gov/articlerender.fcgi?tool=pmcentrez&artid=81663). .

[142] Ross RG (July 2006). "Psychotic and manic-like symptoms during stimulant treatment of attention deficit hyperactivity disorder". *The American Journal of Psychiatry* **163** (7): 1149–52. doi: 10.1176/appi.ajp.163.7.1149 (http://dx.doi.org/10.1176/appi.ajp.163.7.1149). PMID 16816217 (http://www.ncbi.nlm.nih.gov/pubmed/16816217).

[143] Wilens TE, Adler LA, Adams J (January 2008). "Misuse and diversion of stimulants prescribed for ADHD: a systematic review of the literature". *Journal of the American Academy of Child and Adolescent Psychiatry* **47** (1): 21–31. doi: 10.1097/chi.0b013e31815a56f1 (http:// dx.doi.org/10.1097/chi.0b013e31815a56f1). PMID 18174822 (http://www.ncbi.nlm.nih.gov/pubmed/18174822).

[144] Solanto MV (July 1998). "Neuropsychopharmacological mechanisms of stimulant drug action in attention-deficit hyperactivity disorder: a review and integration". *Behavioural Brain Research* **94** (1): 127–52. doi: 10.1016/S0166-4328(97)00175-7 (http://dx.doi.org/10.1016/ S0166-4328(97)00175-7). PMID 9708845 (http://www.ncbi.nlm.nih.gov/pubmed/9708845).

[145] " NIMH · ADHD · The Treatment of ADHD (http://www.nimh.nih.gov/health/publications/attention-deficit-hyperactivity-disorder/ medications.shtml)". .

[146] Murphy, Kevin R.; Barkley, Russell A. (2005). *Attention-Deficit Hyperactivity Disorder, Third Edition : A Clinical Workbook* (http:// books.google.ca/books?id=EkyTTvjNRZAC&pg=PA626&lpg=PA626&dq=long+term+safety+of+stimulants&source=web&

ots=AFB-MtfAvw&sig=J5rqYBXyT3bjYKtFmFmEJ33s5Zk&hl=en&sa=X&oi=book_result&resnum=5&ct=result#PPA626,M1). New York: The Guilford Press. ISBN 1-59385-227-4. .

[147] " What is the evidence for using CNS stimulants to treat ADHD in children? | Therapeutics Initiative (http://www.ti.ubc.ca/letter69)". .

[148] Lerner M, Wigal T (January 2008). "Long-term safety of stimulant medications used to treat children with ADHD". *Pediatric annals* **37** (1): 37–45. doi: 10.3928/00904481-20080101-11 (http://dx.doi.org/10.3928/00904481-20080101-11). PMID 18240852 (http://www.ncbi.nlm.nih.gov/pubmed/18240852).

[149] " FDA News (http://www.fda.gov/NewsEvents/Newsroom/PressAnnouncements/2007/ucm108849.htm)". FDA. February 21, 2007. . Retrieved 2009-08-14.

[150] " Drugs with Black Box Warnings - Comprehensive List (http://www.formularyproductions.com/master/showpage.php?dir=blackbox&whichpage=9)". *FormWeb*. Joyce Generali. 5/4/2009. . Retrieved 2009-05-19.

[151] American Academy of Pediatrics/American Heart Association (August 2008). "American Academy of Pediatrics/American Heart Association clarification of statement on cardiovascular evaluation and monitoring of children and adolescents with heart disease receiving medications for ADHD: May 16, 2008". *Journal of Developmental and Behavioral Pediatrics* **29** (4): 335. doi: 10.1097/DBP.0b013e31318185dc14 (http://dx.doi.org/10.1097/DBP.0b013e31318185dc14). PMID 18698199 (http://www.ncbi.nlm.nih.gov/pubmed/18698199).

[152] *WebMD - Antipsychotic Drug Use Rising Among ADHD Kids* (http://www.webmd.com/add-adhd/news/20040802/antipsychotic-drug-use-rising-among-adhd-kids)

[153] *Pharmalot - Florida Medicaid To Review Antipsychotics & ADHD* (http://www.pharmalot.com/2008/01/florida-medicaid-to-review-antipsychotics-adhd/)

[154] Stein MA (July 2004). " Innovations in attention-deficit/hyperactivity disorder pharmacotherapy: long-acting stimulant and nonstimulant treatments (http://www.ajmc.com/pubMed.php?pii=2632)". *The American Journal of Managed Care* **10** (4 Suppl): S89–98. PMID 15352535 (http://www.ncbi.nlm.nih.gov/pubmed/15352535). .

[155] Christman AK, Fermo JD, Markowitz JS (August 2004). "Atomoxetine, a novel treatment for attention-deficit-hyperactivity disorder". *Pharmacotherapy* **24** (8): 1020–36. doi: 10.1592/phco.24.11.1020.36146 (http://dx.doi.org/10.1592/phco.24.11.1020.36146). PMID 15338851 (http://www.ncbi.nlm.nih.gov/pubmed/15338851).

[156] Hazell P (October 2005). "Do adrenergically active drugs have a role in the first-line treatment of attention-deficit/hyperactivity disorder?". *Expert Opinion on Pharmacotherapy* **6** (12): 1989–98. doi: 10.1517/14656566.6.12.1989 (http://dx.doi.org/10.1517/14656566.6.12.1989). PMID 16197353 (http://www.ncbi.nlm.nih.gov/pubmed/16197353).

[157] " Atomoxetine (marketed as Strattera) Information (http://www.fda.gov/Drugs/DrugSafety/PostmarketDrugSafetyInformationforPatientsandProviders/ucm107912.htm)". . Retrieved 12 July 2009.

[158] Biederman J, Swanson JM, Wigal SB, Boellner SW, Earl CQ, Lopez FA (May 2006). " A comparison of once-daily and divided doses of modafinil in children with attention-deficit/hyperactivity disorder: a randomized, double-blind, and placebo-controlled study (http://article.psychiatrist.com/?ContentType=START&ID=10002551)". *The Journal of Clinical Psychiatry* **67** (5): 727–35. PMID 16841622 (http://www.ncbi.nlm.nih.gov/pubmed/16841622). .

[159] Greenhill LL, Biederman J, Boellner SW (May 2006). "A randomized, double-blind, placebo-controlled study of modafinil film-coated tablets in children and adolescents with attention-deficit/hyperactivity disorder". *Journal of the American Academy of Child and Adolescent Psychiatry* **45** (5): 503–11. doi: 10.1097/01.chi.0000205709.63571.c9 (http://dx.doi.org/10.1097/01.chi.0000205709.63571.c9). PMID 16601402 (http://www.ncbi.nlm.nih.gov/pubmed/16601402).

[160] " Modavigil Product Information (http://secure.healthlinks.net.au/content/csl/pi.cfm?product=cspmodav11207)". . Retrieved 2008-07-02.

[161] Johnson M, Ostlund S, Fransson G, Kadesjö B, Gillberg C (March 2009). "Omega-3/omega-6 fatty acids for attention deficit hyperactivity disorder: a randomized placebo-controlled trial in children and adolescents". *Journal of Attention Disorders* **12** (5): 394–401. doi: 10.1177/1087054708316261 (http://dx.doi.org/10.1177/1087054708316261). PMID 18448859 (http://www.ncbi.nlm.nih.gov/pubmed/18448859).

[162] "Diet and attention deficit hyperactivity disorder." *Harvard Mental Health Letter.* June 2009

[163] " FDA Asks Attention-Deficit Hyperactivity Disorder (ADHD) Drug Manufacturers to Develop Patient Medication Guides (http://www.fda.gov/cder/drug/infopage/ADHD/default.htm)". FDA. September 21, 2007. . Retrieved 2009-04-13.

[164] S. HIRAYAMA,Y. MASUDA,R. RABELER. " Effect of phosphatidylserine administration on symptoms of Attention-deficit/hyperactivity disorder in children (http://d.wanfangdata.com.cn/NSTLQK_NSTL_QK13391780.aspx)". *Agro Food* **17** (5): 32–36. .

[165] Health benefits : PS (http://wiki.verkata.com/en/wiki/Phosphatidylserine)

[166] Greydanus DE, Pratt HD, Patel DR (February 2007). "Attention deficit hyperactivity disorder across the lifespan: the child, adolescent, and adult". *Disease-a-month* **53** (2): 70–131. doi: 10.1016/j.disamonth.2007.01.001 (http://dx.doi.org/10.1016/j.disamonth.2007.01.001). PMID 17386306 (http://www.ncbi.nlm.nih.gov/pubmed/17386306).

[167] Loo SK, Barkley RA (2005). "Clinical utility of EEG in attention deficit hyperactivity disorder". *Appl Neuropsychol* **12** (2): 64–76. doi: 10.1207/s15324826an1202_2 (http://dx.doi.org/10.1207/s15324826an1202_2). PMID 16083395 (http://www.ncbi.nlm.nih.gov/pubmed/16083395).

[168] Holtmann M, Stadler C (April 2006). "Electroencephalographic biofeedback for the treatment of attention-deficit hyperactivity disorder in childhood and adolescence". *Expert Review of Neurotherapeutics* **6** (4): 533–40. doi: 10.1586/14737175.6.4.533 (http://dx.doi.org/10.

1586/14737175.6.4.533). PMID 16623652 (http://www.ncbi.nlm.nih.gov/pubmed/16623652).

[169] Holtmann M, Stadler C, Leins U, Strehl U, Birbaumer N, Poustka F (July 2004). "[Neurofeedback for the treatment of attention-deficit/hyperactivity disorder (ADHD) in childhood and adolescence]" (in German). *Zeitschrift Für Kinder- Und Jugendpsychiatrie Und Psychotherapie* **32** (3): 187–200. doi: 10.1024/1422-4917.32.3.187 (http://dx.doi.org/10.1024/1422-4917.32.3.187). PMID 15357015 (http://www.ncbi.nlm.nih.gov/pubmed/15357015).

[170] Fox DJ, Tharp DF, Fox LC (December 2005). "Neurofeedback: an alternative and efficacious treatment for Attention Deficit Hyperactivity Disorder". *Applied Psychophysiology and Biofeedback* **30** (4): 365–73. doi: 10.1007/s10484-005-8422-3 (http://dx.doi.org/10.1007/s10484-005-8422-3). PMID 16385424 (http://www.ncbi.nlm.nih.gov/pubmed/16385424).

[171] Heinrich H, Gevensleben H, Freisleder FJ, Moll GH, Rothenberger A (April 2004). "Training of slow cortical potentials in attention-deficit/hyperactivity disorder: evidence for positive behavioral and neurophysiological effects". *Biological Psychiatry* **55** (7): 772–5. doi: 10.1016/j.biopsych.2003.11.013 (http://dx.doi.org/10.1016/j.biopsych.2003.11.013). PMID 15039008 (http://www.ncbi.nlm.nih.gov/pubmed/15039008).

[172] Hillman CH, Buck SM, Themanson JR, Pontifex MB, Castelli DM (January 2009). "Aerobic fitness and cognitive development: Event-related brain potential and task performance indices of executive control in preadolescent children". *Developmental Psychology* **45** (1): 114–29. doi: 10.1037/a0014437 (http://dx.doi.org/10.1037/a0014437). PMID 19209995 (http://www.ncbi.nlm.nih.gov/pubmed/19209995).

[173] Lopez-Williams, A.; Chacko, A.; Wymbs, B. T.; Fabiano, G. A.; Seymour, K. E.; Gnagy, E. M.; Chronis, A. M.; Burrows-Maclean, L. *et al.* (2005). "Athletic Performance and Social Behavior as Predictors of Peer Acceptance in Children Diagnosed With Attention-Deficit/Hyperactivity Disorder". *Journal of Emotional and Behavioral Disorders* **13**: 173. doi: 10.1177/10634266050130030501 (http://dx.doi.org/10.1177/10634266050130030501).

[174] Zimmerman FJ, Christakis DA (November 2007). "Associations between content types of early media exposure and subsequent attentional problems". *Pediatrics* **120** (5): 986–92. doi: 10.1542/peds.2006-3322 (http://dx.doi.org/10.1542/peds.2006-3322). PMID 17974735 (http://www.ncbi.nlm.nih.gov/pubmed/17974735).

[175] " ADHD's Outdoor Cure (http://www.psychologytoday.com/articles/200404/adhds-outdoor-cure)". Psychology Today. March 1, 2004. . Retrieved 2009-11-11.

[176] Molina BS, Hinshaw SP, Swanson JM (May 2009). "The MTA at 8 years: prospective follow-up of children treated for combined-type ADHD in a multisite study". *Journal of the American Academy of Child and Adolescent Psychiatry* **48** (5): 484–500. doi: 10.1097/CHI.0b013e31819c23d0 (http://dx.doi.org/10.1097/CHI.0b013e31819c23d0). PMID 19318991 (http://www.ncbi.nlm.nih.gov/pubmed/19318991).

[177] http://web.archive.org/web/20070621111922/http://www.eric.ed.gov/ERICDocs/data/ericdocs2/content_storage_01/0000000b/80/22/94/d6.pdfPDF (562 KB)

[178] Cimera, Robert (2002). *Making ADHD a gift: teaching Superman how to fly* (http://www.rowmaneducation.com/Catalog/SingleBook.shtml?command=Search&db=^DB/CATALOG.db&eqSKUdata=0810843196). Lanham, Maryland: Scarecrow Press, Inc.. p. 116. ISBN 0810843188. . Retrieved 2009-05-02.

[179] College Degree Nearly Doubles Annual Earnings, Census Bureau Reports (http://www.census.gov/Press-Release/www/releases/archives/education/004214.html) U.S. Census Bureau March 28, 2005. Retrieved on 2008-08-02.

[180] ContinuingEdCourses.net (http://www.continuingedcourses.net/active/courses/course034.php)

[181] ContinuingEdCourses.net (http://www.continuingedcourses.net)

[182] Polanczyk G, de Lima MS, Horta BL, Biederman J, Rohde LA (June 2007). "The worldwide prevalence of ADHD: a systematic review and metaregression analysis". *The American Journal of Psychiatry* **164** (6): 942–8. doi: 10.1176/appi.ajp.164.6.942 (http://dx.doi.org/10.1176/appi.ajp.164.6.942). PMID 17541055 (http://www.ncbi.nlm.nih.gov/pubmed/17541055).

[183] " ADHD Home (http://www.cdc.gov/ncbddd/ADHD/)". .

[184] " CDC.gov (http://www.cdc.gov/nchs/data/series/sr_10/sr10_221.pdf)" (PDF). .

[185] Staller J, Faraone SV (2006). "Attention-deficit hyperactivity disorder in girls: epidemiology and management". *CNS Drugs* **20** (2): 107–23. doi: 10.2165/00023210-200620020-00003 (http://dx.doi.org/10.2165/00023210-200620020-00003). PMID 16478287 (http://www.ncbi.nlm.nih.gov/pubmed/16478287).

[186] NICE 2008 Pg. 134

[187] http://en.wikipedia.org/wiki/Attention-deficit_hyperactivity_disorder

[188] Saletan, William (2009-01-12). " Doping Deficit Disorder. Need performance-enhancing drugs? Claim ADHD (http://www.slate.com/id/2208429/)". Slate. . Retrieved 2009-05-02.

[189] An Early Description of ADHD (Inattentive Subtype): Dr Alexander Crichton and `Mental Restlessness' (1798) Child and Adolescent Mental Health (http://www.ingentaconnect.com/search/article?title=Crichton&title_type=tka&year_from=1998&year_to=2008&database=1&pageSize=20&index=14), Volume 6, Number 2, May 2001 , pp. 66–73(8)

[190] p 271, An inquiry into the nature and origin of mental derangement: comprehending a concise system of the physiology and pathology of the human mind and a history of the passions and their effects.

[191] " Development of the DSM (http://kadi.myweb.uga.edu/The_Development_of_the_DSM.html)". Kadi.myweb.uga.edu. . Retrieved 2009-05-25.

[192] Patrick KS, Straughn AB, Perkins JS, González MA (January 2009). " Evolution of stimulants to treat ADHD: transdermal methylphenidate (http://www.pubmedcentral.nih.gov/articlerender.fcgi?tool=pmcentrez&artid=2629554)". *Human Psychopharmacology*

24 (1): 1–17. doi: 10.1002/hup.992 (http://dx.doi.org/10.1002/hup.992). PMID 19051222 (http://www.ncbi.nlm.nih.gov/pubmed/19051222).

[193] " Defining and Diagnosing ADHD (http://www.pbs.org/wgbh/pages/frontline/shows/medicating/adhd/)". PBS. . Retrieved 2009-05-25.

[194] " Opponents and Backlash (http://www.pbs.org/wgbh/pages/frontline/shows/medicating/backlash)". PBS. . Retrieved 2009-05-25.

[195] Castellanos, Xavier. Interview. *Interviews: Xavier Castellanos, M.D.* (http://www.pbs.org/wgbh/pages/frontline/shows/medicating/interviews/castellanos.html). PBS. 2000-10-10. Retrieved on 2009-05-25.

[196] " 'I'm passionate about life' (http://www.msnbc.msn.com/id/8343367/page/2/)". msnbc.msn.com. . Retrieved 2008-12-30.

[197] " Health | Peer calls for ADHD care review (http://news.bbc.co.uk/1/low/health/7093944.stm)". BBC News. 2007-11-14. . Retrieved 2009-05-25.

[198] " Baroness Susan Greenfield (http://www.brunel.ac.uk/about/hongrads/2000/greenfield)". Brunel.ac.uk. . Retrieved 2009-05-25.

[199] Foreman DM (February 2006). " Attention deficit hyperactivity disorder: legal and ethical aspects (http://www.pubmedcentral.nih.gov/articlerender.fcgi?tool=pmcentrez&artid=2082674)". *Archives of Disease in Childhood* **91** (2): 192–4. doi: 10.1136/adc.2004.064576 (http://dx.doi.org/10.1136/adc.2004.064576). PMID 16428370 (http://www.ncbi.nlm.nih.gov/pubmed/16428370).

[200] " Controversies Surrounding ADHD - (ADHD) Attention Deficit Hyperactivity Disorder Cause, Diagnosis, History (http://www.mentalhelp.net/poc/view_doc.php?type=doc&id=13852&cn=3)". .

[201] Ashton H, Gallagher P, Moore B (September 2006). " The adult psychiatrist's dilemma: psychostimulant use in attention deficit/hyperactivity disorder (http://jop.sagepub.com/cgi/content/abstract/20/5/602)". *J. Psychopharmacol. (Oxford)* **20** (5): 602–10. doi: 10.1177/0269881106061710 (http://dx.doi.org/10.1177/0269881106061710). PMID 16478756 (http://www.ncbi.nlm.nih.gov/pubmed/16478756). .

[202] Lakhan SE, Hagger-Johnson GE (2007). " The impact of prescribed psychotropics on youth (http://www.cpementalhealth.com/content/3/1/21)". *Clin Pract Epidemol Ment Health* **3**: 21. doi: 10.1186/1745-0179-3-21 (http://dx.doi.org/10.1186/1745-0179-3-21). PMID 17949504 (http://www.ncbi.nlm.nih.gov/pubmed/17949504). PMC 2100041 (http://www.pubmedcentral.nih.gov/articlerender.fcgi?tool=pmcentrez&artid=2100041). .

[203] National Institutes of Health (NIH) (http://consensus.nih.gov/1998/1998AttentionDeficitHyperactivityDisorder110PDF.pdf) | title=Diagnosis and Treatment of Attention Deficit Hyperactivity Disorder (ADHD). NIH Consensus Statement 1998 Nov 16Ð18; 16(2): 1Ð37.

[204] Reason R; Working Party of the British Psychological Society (1999). "ADHD: a psychological response to an evolving concept. (Report of a Working Party of the British Psychological Society)". *Journal of Learning Disabilities* **32** (1): 85–91. doi: 10.1177/002221949903200108 (http://dx.doi.org/10.1177/002221949903200108). PMID 15499890 (http://www.ncbi.nlm.nih.gov/pubmed/15499890).

[205] Encyclopedia - Britannica Online Encyclopedia (http://www.britannica.com/EBchecked/topic/279477/attention-deficithyperactivity-disorder/216017/Controversy-mental-disorder-or-state-of-mind)

[206] Nice.org.uk (http://www.nice.org.uk/nicemedia/pdf/ADHDFullGuideline.pdf), National Institute for Clinical Excellence (NICE)

Bibliography

- Dr Jennifer Erkulwater; Dr Rick Mayes; Dr Catherine Bagwell (2009). *Medicating Children: ADHD and Pediatric Mental Health.* Cambridge: Harvard University Press. pp. 5. ISBN 0-674-03163-6.

Further reading

- Barkley, Russell A. *Take Charge of ADHD: The Complete Authoritative Guide for Parents* (2005) New York: Guilford Publications.
- Conrad, Peter *Identifying Hyperactive Children* (Ashgate, 2006).
- Crawford, Teresa *I'm Not Stupid! I'm ADHD!*
- Faraone, Stephen V. (2005). *The scientific foundation for understanding attention-deficit/hyperactivity disorder as a valid psychiatric disorder.* Eur Child Adolesc Psychiatry 14, 1-10.
- Faraone, Stephen, V.*Straight Talk about Your Child's Mental Health: What to Do When Something Seems Wrong* (2003) New York:Guilford Press
- Green, Christopher, Kit Chee, *Understanding ADD*; Doubleday 1994; ISBN 0-86824-587-9
- Hanna, Mohab. (2006) *Making the Connection: A Parent's Guide to Medication in ADHD*, Washington D.C.: Ladner-Drysdale.
- Hartmann, Thom (2003). *The Edison gene: ADHD and the gift of the hunter child.* Rochester, Vt: Park Street Press. ISBN 0-89281-128-5.
- Matlen, Terry. (2005) "Survival Tips for Women with AD/HD". ISBN 1-886941-59-9

- Ninivaggi, F.J. "Attention-Deficit/Hyperactivity Disorder in Children and Adolescents: Rethinking Diagnosis and Treatment Implications for Complicated Cases", *Connecticut Medicine*. September 1999; Vol. 63, No. 9, 515-521. PMID 10531701
- Southall, Angela (2007). *The Other Side of ADHD:Attention Deficit Hyperactivity Disorder Exposed and Explained* (http://books.google.ca/books?id=AKXhThWgvyYC&pg=PA41&lpg=PA41&dq=barkley+drug+company+funding&source=bl&ots=X-Twuf7Jvx&sig=FE3J6Ov1puhnrxC3c-464VbbVaE&hl=en&sa=X&oi=book_result&resnum=1&ct=result#PPP1,M1). Radcliffe Publishing Ltd. ISBN 1846190681. Retrieved 2009-05-02.

Adult ADHD

- Kelly, Kate, Peggy Ramundo. (1993) *You Mean I'm Not Lazy, Stupid or Crazy?! A Self-Help Book for Adults with Attention deficit Disorder.* ISBN 0-684-81531-1
- Ratey, Nancy. (2008) *The Disorganized Mind: Coaching Your ADHD Brain to Take Control of Your Time, Tasks, and Talents.* ISBN 0312355335
- Weiss, Lynn. (2005) *Attention Deficit Disorder in Adults, 4th Edition: A Different Way of Thinking* ISBN 1589792378

External links

- National Institute of Mental Health on ADHD (http://www.nimh.nih.gov/publicat/adhd.cfm)
- " CG72 Attention deficit hyperactivity disorder (ADHD): full guideline (http://www.nice.org.uk/nicemedia/pdf/ADHDFullGuideline.pdf)" (PDF). NHS. 09 March 2009. Retrieved 2009-01-08.
- New Zealand MOH Guidelines for the Assessment and Treatment of Attention-Deficit/Hyperactivity Disorder (http://www.moh.govt.nz/moh.nsf/c7ad5e032528c34c4c2566690076db9b/4e1c3cddf420bcaecc256a8e007f12d9/$FILE/ADHDGuidelines.pdf)

Speak to Julie 8.

ıgnostic and Statistical Manual of Mental Disorders

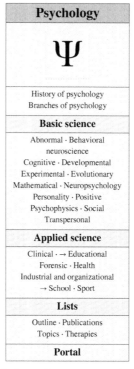

Psychology
Ψ
History of psychology Branches of psychology
Basic science
Abnormal · Behavioral neuroscience Cognitive · Developmental Experimental · Evolutionary Mathematical · Neuropsychology Personality · Positive Psychophysics · Social Transpersonal
Applied science
Clinical · → Educational Forensic · Health Industrial and organizational → School · Sport
Lists
Outline · Publications Topics · Therapies
Portal

The *Diagnostic and Statistical Manual of Mental Disorders* (**DSM**) is published by the American Psychiatric Association and provides diagnostic criteria for mental disorders. It is used in the United States and in varying degrees around the world, by clinicians, researchers, psychiatric drug regulation agencies, health insurance companies, pharmaceutical companies and policy makers.

The DSM has attracted controversy and criticism as well as praise. There have been five revisions since it was first published in 1952, gradually including more disorders, though some have been removed and are no longer considered to be mental disorders. It initially evolved out of systems for collecting census and psychiatric hospital statistics, and from a manual developed by the US Army. The last major revision was the fourth edition ("DSM-IV"), published in 1994, although a "text revision" was produced in 2000. The fifth edition ("DSM-V") is currently in consultation, planning and preparation, due for publication in May 2012.[1] The mental disorders section of the International Statistical Classification of Diseases and Related Health Problems (ICD) is another commonly-used guide, used more often in Europe and other parts of the world. The coding system used in the DSM-IV is designed to correspond with the codes used in the ICD, although not all codes may match at all times because the two publications are not revised synchronously.

Uses

Many mental health professionals use this book to determine and help communicate a patient's diagnosis after an evaluation; hospitals, clinics, and insurance companies also generally require a 'five axis' DSM diagnosis of all the patients treated. The DSM can be used to establish a diagnosis or categorize patients using diagnostic criteria. The DSM may also be used in mental health research. Studies done on specific diseases often recruit patients whose symptoms match the criteria listed in the DSM for that disease. An international survey of psychiatrists in 66 countries comparing use of the ICD-10 and DSM-IV found the former was more often used for clinical diagnosis while the latter was more valued for research.[2]

The DSM, including DSM-IV, is a registered trademark belonging to the American Psychiatric Association.[3]

History

The initial impetus for developing a classification of mental disorders in the United States was the need to collect statistical information. The first official attempt was the 1840 census which used a single category, "idiocy/insanity". The 1880 census distinguished among seven categories: mania, melancholia, monomania, paresis, dementia, dipsomania, and epilepsy. In 1917, a "Committee on Statistics" from what is now known as the American Psychiatric Association (APA), together with the National Commission on Mental Hygiene, developed a new guide for mental hospitals called the "Statistical Manual for the Use of Institutions for the Insane", which included 22 diagnoses. This was subsequently revised several times by APA over the years. APA, along with the New York Academy of Medicine, also provided the psychiatric nomenclature subsection of the US medical guide, the "Standard Classified Nomenclature of Disease", referred to as the "Standard".[4]

DSM-I (1952)

World War II saw the large-scale involvement of US psychiatrists in the selection, processing, assessment and treatment of soldiers. This moved the focus away from mental institutions and traditional clinical perspectives. A committee headed by psychiatrist and brigadier general William C. Menninger developed a new classification scheme called **Medical 203**, issued in 1943 as a "War Department Technical Bulletin" under the auspices of the Office of the Surgeon General.[5] The foreword to the DSM-I states the US Navy had itself made some minor revisions but "the Army established a much more sweeping revision, abandoning the basic outline of the Standard and attempting to express present day concepts of mental disturbance. This nomenclature eventually was adopted by all Armed Forces", and "assorted modifications of the Armed Forces nomenclature [were] introduced into many clinics and hospitals by psychiatrists returning from military duty." The Veterans Administration also adopted a slightly modified version of Medical 203.

In 1949, the World Health Organization published the sixth revision of the International Statistical Classification of Diseases (ICD) which included a section on mental disorders for the first time. The foreword to DSM-1 states this "categorized mental disorders in rubrics similar to those of the Armed Forces nomenclature." An APA Committee on Nomenclature and Statistics was empowered to develop a version specifically for use in the United States, to standardize the diverse and confused usage of different documents. In 1950 the APA committee undertook a review and consultation. It circulated an adaptation of Medical 203, the VA system and the Standard's Nomenclature, to approximately 10% of APA members. 46% replied, of which 93% approved, and after some further revisions (resulting in it being called DSM-I), the Diagnostic and Statistical Manual of Mental Disorders was approved in 1951 and published in 1952. The structure and conceptual framework were the same as in Medical 203, and many passages of text identical.[5] The manual was 130 pages long and listed 106 mental disorders.[6]

DSM-II (1968)

Although the APA was closely involved in the next significant revision of the mental disorder section of the ICD (version 8 in 1968), it decided to also go ahead with a revision of the DSM. It was also published in 1968, listed 182 disorders, and was 134 pages long. It was quite similar to the DSM-I. The term "reaction" was dropped but the term "neurosis" was retained. Both the DSM-I and the DSM-II reflected the predominant psychodynamic psychiatry,[7] although they also included biological perspectives and concepts from Kraepelin's system of classification. Symptoms were not specified in detail for specific disorders. Many were seen as reflections of broad underlying conflicts or maladaptive reactions to life problems, rooted in a distinction between neurosis and psychosis (roughly, anxiety/depression broadly in touch with reality, or hallucinations/delusions appearing disconnected from reality). Sociological and biological knowledge was also incorporated, in a model that did not emphasize a clear boundary between normality and abnormality.[8]

Following controversy and protests from gay activists at APA annual conferences from 1970 to 1973, as well as the emergence of new data from researchers such as Alfred Kinsey and Evelyn Hooker, the seventh printing of the DSM-II, in 1974, no longer listed homosexuality as a category of disorder. But through the efforts of psychiatrist Robert Spitzer, who had led the DSM-II development committee, a vote by the APA trustees in 1973, and confirmed by the wider APA membership in 1974, the diagnosis was replaced with the category of "sexual orientation disturbance",[9] presently referred to as gender identity disorder (GID).

DSM-III (1980)

In 1974, the decision to create a new revision of the DSM was made, and Robert Spitzer was selected as chairman of the task force. The initial impetus was to make the DSM nomenclature consistent with the International Statistical Classification of Diseases and Related Health Problems (ICD), published by the World Health Organization. The revision took on a far wider mandate under the influence and control of Spitzer and his chosen committee members.[10] One goal was to improve the uniformity and validity of psychiatric diagnosis in the wake of a number of critiques, including the famous Rosenhan experiment. There was also a need to standardize diagnostic practices within the US and with other countries after research showed that psychiatric diagnoses differed markedly between Europe and the USA.[11] The establishment of these criteria was also an attempt to facilitate the pharmaceutical regulatory process.

The criteria adopted for many of the mental disorders were taken from the Research Diagnostic Criteria (RDC) and Feighner Criteria, which had just been developed by a group of research-orientated psychiatrists based primarily at Washington University in St. Louis and the New York State Psychiatric Institute. Other criteria, and potential new categories of disorder, were established by consensus during meetings of the committee, as chaired by Spitzer. A key aim was to base categorization on colloquial English descriptive language (which would be easier to use by Federal administrative offices), rather than assumptions of etiology, although its categorical approach assumed each particular pattern of symptoms in a category reflected a particular underlying pathology (an approach described as "neo-Kraepelinian"). The psychodynamic or physiologic view was abandoned, in favor of a regulatory or legislative model. A new "multiaxial" system attempted to yield a picture more amenable to a statistical population census, rather than just a simple diagnosis. Spitzer argued, "mental disorders are a subset of medical disorders" but the task force decided on the DSM statement: "Each of the mental disorders is conceptualized as a clinically significant behavioral or psychological syndrome."[7]

The first draft of the DSM-III was prepared within a year. Many new categories of disorder were introduced; a number of the unpublished documents that aim to justify them have recently come to light.[12] Field trials sponsored by the U.S. National Institute of Mental Health (NIMH) were conducted between 1977 and 1979 to test the reliability of the new diagnoses. A controversy emerged regarding deletion of the concept of neurosis, a mainstream of psychoanalytic theory and therapy but seen as vague and unscientific by the DSM task force. Faced with enormous political opposition, so the DSM-III was in serious danger of not being approved by the APA Board of

Trustees unless "neurosis" was included in some capacity, a political compromise reinserted the term in parentheses after the word "disorder" in some cases. Additionally, the diagnosis of ego-dystonic homosexuality replaced the DSM-II category of "sexual orientation disturbance".

Finally published in 1980, the DSM-III was 494 pages long and listed 265 diagnostic categories. It rapidly came into widespread international use by multiple stakeholders and has been termed a revolution or transformation in psychiatry.[7] [8] .

DSM-III-R (1987)

In 1987 the DSM-III-R was published as a revision of DSM-III, under the direction of Spitzer. Categories were renamed, reorganized, and significant changes in criteria were made. Six categories were deleted while others were added. Controversial diagnoses such as pre-menstrual dysphoric disorder and Masochistic Personality Disorder were considered and discarded. "Sexual orientation disturbance" was also removed, but was largely subsumed under "sexual disorder not otherwise specified" which can include "persistent and marked distress about one's sexual orientation."[7] [13] Altogether, DSM-III-R contained 292 diagnoses and was 567 pages long.

DSM-IV (1994)

In 1994, DSM-IV was published, listing 297 disorders in 886 pages. The task force was chaired by Allen Frances. A steering committee of 27 people was introduced, including four psychologists. The steering committee created 13 work groups of 5–16 members. Each work group had approximately 20 advisers. The work groups conducted a three step process. First, each group conducted an extensive literature review of their diagnoses. Then they requested data from researchers, conducting analyses to determine which criteria required change, with instructions to be conservative. Finally, they conducted multicenter field trials relating diagnoses to clinical practice.[14] [15] A major change from previous versions was the inclusion of a clinical significance criterion to almost half of all the categories, which required symptoms cause "clinically significant distress or impairment in social, occupational, or other important areas of functioning".

DSM-IV-TR (2000)

A "Text Revision" of the DSM-IV, known as the DSM-IV-TR, was published in 2000. The diagnostic categories and the vast majority of the specific criteria for diagnosis were unchanged.[16] The text sections giving extra information on each diagnosis were updated, as were some of the diagnostic codes in order to maintain consistency with the ICD.

DSM-IV-TR - The Current Version

Categorization

The DSM-IV is a categorical classification system. The categories are prototypes, and a patient with a close approximation to the prototype is said to have that disorder. DSM-IV states, "there is no assumption each category of mental disorder is a completely discrete entity with absolute boundaries..." but isolated, low-grade and noncriterion (unlisted for a given disorder) symptoms are not given importance.[17] Qualifiers are sometimes used, for example mild, moderate or severe forms of a disorder. For nearly half the disorders, symptoms must be sufficient to cause "clinically significant distress or impairment in social, occupational, or other important areas of functioning", although DSM-IV-TR removed the distress criterion from tic disorders and several of the paraphilias. Each category of disorder has a numeric code taken from the ICD coding system, used for health service (including insurance) administrative purposes.

DSM-IV-TR, the current DSM edition

Multi-axial system

The DSM-IV organizes each psychiatric diagnosis into five levels (axes) relating to different aspects of disorder or disability:

- *Axis I:* clinical disorders, including major mental disorders, as well as developmental and learning disorders
- *Axis II:* underlying pervasive or personality conditions, as well as mental retardation
- *Axis III:* acute medical conditions and physical disorders
- *Axis IV:* psychosocial and environmental factors contributing to the disorder
- *Axis V:* Global Assessment of Functioning or Children's Global Assessment Scale for children and teens under the age of 18

Common Axis I disorders include depression, anxiety disorders, bipolar disorder, ADHD, autism, phobias, and schizophrenia.

Common Axis II disorders include personality disorders: paranoid personality disorder, schizoid personality disorder, schizotypal personality disorder, borderline personality disorder, antisocial personality disorder, narcissistic personality disorder, histrionic personality disorder, avoidant personality disorder, dependent personality disorder, obsessive-compulsive personality disorder, and mental retardation.

Common Axis III disorders include brain injuries and other medical/physical disorders which may aggravate existing diseases or present symptoms similar to other disorders.

Cautions

The **DSM-IV-TR** states, because it is produced for the completion of Federal legislative mandates, its use by people without clinical training can lead to inappropriate application of its contents. Appropriate use of the diagnostic criteria is said to require extensive clinical training, and its contents "cannot simply be applied in a cookbook fashion".[18] *The APA notes diagnostic labels are primarily for use as a "convenient shorthand" among professionals.* The DSM advises laypersons should consult the DSM only to obtain information, not to make diagnoses, and people who may have a mental disorder should be referred to psychological counseling or treatment. Further, a shared diagnosis/label may have different etiologies (causes) or require different treatments; the DSM contains no information regarding treatment or cause for this reason. The range of the DSM represents an extensive scope of psychiatric and psychological issues or conditions, and it is not exclusive to what may be considered "illnesses".

Sourcebooks

The DSM-IV doesn't specifically cite its sources, but there are four volumes of "sourcebooks" intended to be APA's documentation of the guideline development process and supporting evidence, including literature reviews, data analyses and field trials.[19] [20] [21] [22] The Sourcebooks have been said to provide important insights into the character and quality of the decisions that led to the production of DSM-IV, and hence the scientific credibility of contemporary psychiatric classification.[23] [24]

Criticism

Beginning with the problem that there is no single objective diagnostic test for a mental illness in the field of psychiatry — a problem the DSM sidesteps by referring only to "mental disorders", defined as dysfunctional psychological or behavioral patterns — the DSM-IV has come under various criticisms over the years.

Validity and reliability

The most fundamental criticism of the DSM concerns the construct validity and reliability of its diagnostic categories and criteria.[25] [26] [27] Although increasingly standardized, critics argue that the DSM's claim of an empirical foundation is overstated.[23] A reliance on operational definitions necessitates that intuitive concepts such as depression be operationally defined before they can be used in scientific investigation. Such definitions are used as a follow up to a conceptual definition, in which the specific concept is defined as a measurable occurrence. John Stuart Mill pointed out the dangers of believing anything that could be given a name must refer to a thing and Stephen Jay Gould and others have criticized psychologists for doing just that. A committed operationalist would respond that speculation about the thing in itself, or noumenon, should be resisted as *meaningless,* and would comment only on phenomena using operationally defined terms and tables of operationally defined measurements. This line of criticism has also appeared in non-specialist venues. In 1997, Harper's Magazine published an essay, ostensibly a book review of the DSM-IV, that criticized the lack of hard science and the proliferation of disorders. The language of the DSM was described as "simultaneously precise and vague", and the manual itself compared to "a militia's Web page, insofar as it constitutes an alternative reality under siege," and a "fertilizer bomb" against hard science.[28]

Symptomatological bias

By design, the DSM is primarily concerned with the symptoms of mental disorders, it does not attempt to analyze or explain the conditions it lists or even to discuss possible patterns or relationships between and among them. As such, it has been compared to a naturalist's field guide to birds, with similar advantages and disadvantages.[29] The lack of causative or explanatory material, however, is not specific to the DSM, but rather reflects a general lack of pathophysiological understanding of psychiatric disorders. As DSM-III chief architect Robert Spitzer and DSM-IV editor Michael First outlined in 2005, "little progress has been made toward understanding the pathophysiological processes and etiology of mental disorders. If anything, the research has shown the situation is even more complex than initially imagined, and we believe not enough is known to structure the classification of psychiatric disorders according to etiology."[30] The DSM's apparent superficiality is therefore largely a result of necessity, since there is no agreement on a more explanatory classification system.

Despite the lack of consensus, advocates for specific psychopathlogical paradigms have nonetheless faulted the current diagnostic scheme for not incorporating the innovations of their particular models; the most recent example being evolutionary psychologists' criticism that the DSM does not differentiate between genuine cognitive malfunctions and those induced by psychological adaptations, a key distinction within evolutionary psychology, but one widely challenged within general psychology.[31] [32] [33]

Reductionist bias

Despite caveats in the introduction to the DSM, it has long been argued that its system of classification makes unjustified categorical distinctions between disorders, and between normal and abnormal. Although the DSM-V may move away from this categorical approach in some limited areas, some argue that a fully dimensional, spectrum or complaint-oriented approach would better reflect the evidence.[34] [35] [36] [37] Similarly, the current individual symptom-based approach has been argued to not adequately take into account the context in which a person is living, and to what extent there is internal disorder of an individual or a psychological response to adverse situations.[38] [39] Because the level of impairment is often not correlated with symptom counts and can stem from various individual and social factors, the standard of distress or disability can often produce false positives. [40]

Some psychiatrists also argue that current diagnostic standards rely on an exaggerated interpretation of neurophysiological findings and so understate the scientific importance of social-psychological variables.[41] Advocating a more culturally sensitive approach to psychology, critics such as Carl Bell and Marcello Maviglia contend that the cultural and ethnic diversity of individuals is often discounted by researchers and service providers.[42] . In addition, current diagnostic guidelines have been criticized as having a fundamentally Euro-American outlook. Although these guidelines have been widely implemented, opponents argue that even when a diagnostic criteria set is accepted across different cultures, it does not necessarily indicate that the underlying constructs have any validity within those cultures; even reliable application can only prove consistency, not legitimacy.[41] Cross-cultural psychiatrist Arthur Kleinman contends that the Western bias is ironically illustrated in the introduction of cultural factors to the DSM-IV: the fact that disorders or concepts from non-Western or non-mainstream cultures are described as "culture-bound", whereas standard psychiatric diagnoses are given no cultural qualification whatsoever, is to Kleinman revelatory of an underlying assumption that Western cultural phenomena are universal.[43] Kleinman's negative view towards the culture-bound syndrome is largely shared by other cross-cultural critics, common responses included both disappointment over the large number of documented non-Western mental disorders still left out, and frustration that even those included were often misintepreted or misrepresented.[44] Many mainstream psychiatrists have also been dissatisfied with these new culture-bound diagnoses, although not for the same reasons. Robert Spitzer, a lead architect of the DSM-III, has opined that the addition of cultural formulations was an attempt to placate cultural critics, and that they lack any scientific motivation or support. Spitzer also posits that the new culture-bound diagnoses are rarely used in practice, maintaining that the standard diagnoses apply regardless of the culture involved. In general, the mainstream psychiatric opinion remains that if a diagnostic category is valid, cross-cultural factors are either irrelevant or are only significant to specific symptom presentations.[41]

It has also been suggested that the apparent reductionism of the DSM, as well as its substantial expansions, are representative of an increasing medicalization of human nature, a result of disease mongering by drug companies, whose influence on psychiatry has dramatically grown in recent decades.[45] Of the authors who selected and defined the DSM-IV psychiatric disorders, roughly half had had financial relationships with the pharmaceutical industry at one time, raising the prospect of a direct conflict of interest.[46] In 2008, then American Psychiatric Association President Steven Sharfstein released a statement in which he conceded that psychiatrists had "allowed the biopsychosocial model to become the bio-bio-bio model".[47]

Political controversies

There is scientific and political controversy regarding the continued inclusion of sex-related diagnoses such as the paraphilias (sexual fetishes) and hypoactive sexual desire disorder (low sex drive). Critics of these and other controversial diagnoses often cite the DSM's previous inclusion of homosexuality, as well as the APA's eventual decision to remove it, as a precedent for current disputes.[48] That 1974 decision, however, is still challenged by many conservative and religious groups who maintain that homosexuality is in fact a mental disorder.[49] The fact that this diagnostic revision continues to be passionately disputed, so many years after the fact, underscores that any reevaluation of controversial disorders must be viewed as a political as well as scientific decision. Indeed, even Robert Spitzer (psychiatrist), a leading proponent of scientific impartiality in the DSM, conceded that a significant reason that certain diagnoses are not removed from the DSM is because "it would be a public relations disaster for psychiatry".[50]

DSM-V: the next version

The next (fifth) edition of the Diagnostic and Statistical Manual of Mental Disorders (DSM), DSM-V, is currently in consultation, planning and preparation. It is due for publication in May 2012.[1]

See also

- Relational disorder (proposed DSM-V new diagnosis)
- Classification of mental disorders
- Chinese Classification and Diagnostic Criteria of Mental Disorders
- DSM-IV Codes
- GAF Scale
- Psychodynamic Diagnostic Manual
- Structured Clinical Interview for DSM-IV *(SCID)*

External links

- DSM-IV-TR Official Site [51] - American Psychiatric Association
- Diagnostic Criteria from DSM-IV-TR [52]
- DSM-IV Made Easy [53] Summary of diagnostic criteria by James Morrison
- DSM-V Prelude Project [54] - DSM-V Prelude Review Project by American Psychiatric Association
- Topic Center: DSM-V [55]
- Reproduction of Medical 203 [56]
- The DSM-II [57]
- Sections of the DSM-IV-TR [58] on Google Books.
- Widiger: Review DSM-IV Source Book [59]

References

[1] DSM-V: The Future Manual (http://www.psych.org/MainMenu/Research/DSMIV/DSMV.aspx)

[2] Mezzich, Juan E. (2002). " International Surveys on the Use of ICD-10 and Related Diagnostic Systems (http://content.karger.com/ ProdukteDB/produkte.asp?Aktion=ShowAbstract&ArtikelNr=65122&Ausgabe=228600&ProduktNr=224276)" (guest editorial, abstract). *Psychopathology* **35** (2-3): 72–75. doi: 10.1159/000065122 (http://dx.doi.org/10.1159/000065122). . Retrieved 2008-09-02.

[3] " Trademark Electronic Search System (TESS) (http://tess2.uspto.gov/bin/showfield?f=doc&state=k7tj8q.2.1)". . Retrieved 2008-02-08.

[4] Greenberg SA, Shuman DW, Meyer RG. (2004) Unmasking forensic diagnosis. Int J Law Psychiatry. 2004 January-February;27(1):1-15. doi=10.1016/j.ijlp.2004.01.001

[5] Houts, A.C. (2000) Fifty years of psychiatric nomenclature: Reflections on the 1943 War Department Technical Bulletin, Medical 203. (http://www3.interscience.wiley.com/journal/72506618/abstract) Journal of Clinical Psychology, 56 (7), Pages 935 - 967

[6] Grob, GN. (1991) Origins of DSM-I: a study in appearance and reality (http://www.ncbi.nlm.nih.gov/entrez/query.fcgi?db=pubmed& cmd=Retrieve&dopt=AbstractPlus&list_uids=2006685) *Am J Psychiatry*. April;148(4):421–31.

[7] Mayes, R. & Horwitz, AV. (2005) DSM-III and the revolution in the classification of mental illness. (http://www.ncbi.nlm.nih.gov/ entrez/query.fcgi?db=pubmed&cmd=Retrieve&dopt=AbstractPlus&list_uids=15981242) *J Hist Behav Sci* 41(3):249–67.

[8] Wilson, M. (1993) DSM-III and the transformation of American psychiatry: a history. (http://www.ncbi.nlm.nih.gov/entrez/query. fcgi?itool=abstractplus&db=pubmed&cmd=Retrieve&dopt=abstractplus&list_uids=8434655) *Am J Psychiatry*. 1993 March;150(3):399–410.

[9] "The diagnostic status of homosexuality in DSM-III: a reformulation of the issues" (http://ajp.psychiatryonline.org/cgi/content/abstract/ 138/2/210), by R.L. Spitzer, Am J Psychiatry 1981; 138:210-215

[10] Speigel, A. (2005) The Dictionary of Disorder: How one man revolutionized of 2005-01-03. (http://www.newyorker.com/fact/content/ articles/050103fa_fact?050103fa_fact)

[11] Cooper JE, Kendell RE, Gurland BJ, Sartorius N, Farkas T (1969). Cross-national study of diagnosis of the mental disorders: some results from the first comparative investigation (http://ajp.psychiatryonline.org/cgi/reprint/125/10S/30) Am J Psychiatry, vol. 10, Suppl, pp. 21-9 PMID 5774702

[12] Lane, Christopher (2007). *Shyness: How Normal Behavior Became a Sickness*. Yale University Press. pp. 263. ISBN 0300124465.

[13] Spiegel, Alix. (18 January 2002.) "81 Words" (http://www.thislife.org/Radio_Episode.aspx?episode=204). In Ira Glass (producer), "This American Life." Chicago: Chicago Public Radio.

[14] Allen Frances, Avram H. Mack, Ruth Ross, and Michael B. First (2000) The DSM-IV Classification and Psychopharmacology (http:// www.acnp.org/G4/GN401000082/CH081.html).

[15] Schaffer, David (1996) A Participant's Observations: Preparing DSM-IV (http://server03.cpa-apc.org:8080/Publications/Archives/PDF/ 1996/Aug/schaffer.pdf) Can J Psychiatry 1996;41:325–329.

[16] APA Summary of Practice-Relevant Changes to the DSM-IV-TR (http://www.dsmivtr.org/2-3changes.cfm).

[17] Maser, JD. & Patterson, T. (2002) Spectrum and nosology: implications for DSM-V (http://www.ncbi.nlm.nih.gov/entrez/query. fcgi?db=pubmed&cmd=Retrieve&dopt=AbstractPlus&list_uids=12462864) *Psychiatric Clinics of North America*, December, 25(4)p855-885

[18] DSM FAQ (http://www.psych.org/research/dor/dsm/dsm_faqs/faq81301.cfm)

[19] DSM-IV Sourcebook Volume 1 (http://www.appi.org/book.cfm?id=2065)

[20] DSM-IV Sourcebook Volume 2 (http://www.appi.org/book.cfm?id=2071)

[21] DSM-IV Sourcebook Volume 3 (http://www.appi.org/book.cfm?id=2073)

[22] DSM-IV Sourcebook Volume 4 (http://www.ajp.psychiatryonline.org/cgi/content/full/156/10/1655)

[23] Poland, JS. (2001) Review of Volume 1 of DSM-IV sourcebook (http://mentalhelp.net/books/books.php?type=de&id=557)

[24] Poland, JS. (2001) Review of vol 2 of DSM-IV sourcebook (http://mentalhelp.net/poc/view_doc.php?id=996&type=book&cn=74)

[25] Kendell R, Jablensky A. (2003) Distinguishing between the validity and utility of psychiatric diagnoses. *Am J Psychiatry*. January;160(1):4-12. PMID 12505793

[26] Baca-Garcia E, Perez-Rodriguez MM, Basurte-Villamor I, Fernandez del Moral AL, Jimenez-Arriero MA, Gonzalez de Rivera JL, Saiz-Ruiz J, Oquendo MA. (2007) Diagnostic stability of psychiatric disorders in clinical practice. Br J Psychiatry. March;190:210-6. PMID 17329740

[27] Pincus et al. (1998) "Clinical Significance" and DSM-IV (http://archpsyc.ama-assn.org/cgi/content/extract/55/12/1145) *Arch Gen Psychiatry.1998; 55: 1145*

[28] L.J. Davis (February 1997). " 'The Encyclopedia of Insanity — A Psychiatric Handbook Lists a Madness for Everyone.' (http://alumnus. caltech.edu/~rbell/EncyclopediaOfInsanity.html.gz)". *Harpers Magazine*. .

[29] Paul R. McHugh (2005) Striving for Coherence: Psychiatry's Efforts Over Classification (http://jama.ama-assn.org/cgi/content/full/293/ 20/2526?ijkey=e5f8d881d7f6c0d853ce55e1ac5b693c5c53a950&keytype2=tf_ipsecsha) JAMA. 2005;293(no.20)2526-2528.

[30] Spitzer and First (2005) Classification of Psychiatric Disorders. (http://jama.ama-assn.org/cgi/content/full/294/15/1898) JAMA.2005; 294: 1898-1899.

[31] Dominic Murphy, PhD; Steven Stich, PhD (1998) Darwin in the Madhouse (http://ruccs.rutgers.edu/ArchiveFolder/Research Group/ Publications/Mad/Madhouse.html)

[32] Leda Cosmides, PhD; John Tooby, PhD (1999) Toward an Evolutionary Taxonomy of Treatable Conditions "J of Abnormal Psychology." 1999;108(3):453-464. (http://www.psych.ucsb.edu/research/cep/papers/taxonomywakefield99.pdf)

[33] McNally RJ. (2001) On Wakefield's harmful dysfunction analysis of mental disorder. Behav Res Ther. 2001 March;39(3):309-14. PMID 11227812

[34] Spitzer, Robert L, M.D., Williams, Janet B.W, D.S.W., First, Michael B, M.D., Gibbon, Miriam, M.S.W., Biometric Research (http://nyspi. org/AR2001/Biometrics.htm)

[35] Maser, JD & Akiskal, HS. et al. (2002) Spectrum concepts in major mental disorders (http://psych.theclinics.com/issues/ contents?volume=25&issue=4) Psychiatric Clinics of North America, Vol. 25, Special issue 4

[36] Krueger, RF., Watson, D., Barlow, DH. et al. (2005) Toward a Dimensionally Based Taxonomy of Psychopathology (http://content.apa. org/journals/abn/114/4) Journal of Abnormal Psychology Vol 114, Issue 4

[37] Bentall, R. (2006) Madness explained : Why we must reject the Kraepelinian paradigm and replace it with a 'complaint-orientated' approach to understanding mental illness (http://cat.inist.fr/?aModele=afficheN&cpsidt=17441292) Medical hypotheses, vol. 66(2), pp. 220-233

[38] Chodoff, P. (2005) Psychiatric Diagnosis: A 60-Year Perspective (http://pn.psychiatryonline.org/cgi/content/full/40/11/17-a) Psychiatric News June 3, 2005 Volume 40 Number 11, p17

[39] Jerome C. Wakefield, PhD, DSW; Mark F. Schmitz, PhD; Michael B. First, MD; Allan V. Horwitz, PhD (2007) Extending the Bereavement Exclusion for Major Depression to Other Losses: Evidence From the National Comorbidity Survey (http://archpsyc.ama-assn.org/cgi/ content/abstract/64/4/433) Arch Gen Psychiatry. 2007;64:433-440.

[40] Spitzer RL, Wakefield JC. (1999) DSM-IV diagnostic criterion for clinical significance: does it help solve the false positives problem? Am J Psychiatry. 1999 December;156(12):1856-64. PMID 10588397

[41] Widiger TA, Sankis LM (2000). "Adult psychopathology: issues and controversies". Annu Rev Psychol 51: 377–404. doi: 10.1146/annurev.psych.51.1.377 (http://dx.doi.org/10.1146/annurev.psych.51.1.377). PMID 10751976 (http://www.ncbi.nlm.nih. gov/pubmed/10751976).

[42] Shankar Vedantam, Psychiatry's Missing Diagnosis: Patients' Diversity Is Often Discounted (http://www.washingtonpost.com/wp-dyn/ content/article/2005/06/25/AR2005062500982.html) Washington Post: Mind and Culture, June 26

[43] Kleinman A (1997). "Triumph or pyrrhic victory? The inclusion of culture in DSM-IV". Harv Rev Psychiatry 4 (6): 343–4. doi: 10.3109/10673229709030563 (http://dx.doi.org/10.3109/10673229709030563). PMID 9385013 (http://www.ncbi.nlm.nih.gov/ pubmed/9385013).

[44] Bhugra, D. & Munro, A. (1997) Troublesome Disguises: Underdiagnosed Psychiatric Syndromes Blackwell Science Ltd

[45] Healy D (2006) The Latest Mania: Selling Bipolar Disorder (http://medicine.plosjournals.org/perlserv/?request=get-document&doi=10. 1371/journal.pmed.0030185&ct=1) PLoS Med 3(4): e185.

[46] Cosgrove, Lisa, Krimsky, Sheldon,Vijayaraghavan, Manisha, Schneider, Lisa, Financial Ties between DSM-IV Panel Members and the Pharmaceutical Industry (http://www.tufts.edu/~skrimsky/PDF/DSM COI.PDF)

[47] Sharfstein, SS. (2005) Big Pharma and American Psychiatry: The Good, the Bad, and the Ugly (http://pn.psychiatryonline.org/cgi/ content/full/40/16/3) Psychiatric News August 19, 2005 Volume 40 Number 16

[48] Alexander, B. (2008) What's 'normal' sex? Shrinks seek definition Controversy erupts over creation of psychiatric rule book's new edition (http://today.msnbc.msn.com/id/24664654/) MSNBC Today, May.

[49] (http://www.narth.com/docs/mentaldisorder.html)

[50] Kleinplatz, P.J & Moser, C. (2005). Politics versus science: An addendum and response to Drs. Spitzer and Fink. (http://home.netcom. com/~docx2/kM-response.htm) Journal of Psychology and Human Sexuality, 17(3/4), 135-139.

[51] http://psych.org/MainMenu/Research/DSMIV.aspx

[52] http://www.behavenet.com/capsules/disorders/dsm4TRclassification.htm

[53] http://www.neurosurvival.ca/ClinicalAssistant/scales/dsm_IV/dsm_index.html

[54] http://dsm5.org/

[55] http://www.psychiatrictimes.com/dsm-v

[56] http://www3.interscience.wiley.com/journal/72506614/abstract

[57] http://www.psychiatryonline.com/DSMPDF/dsm-ii.pdf

[58] http://books.google.com/books?id=3SQrtpnHb9MC&printsec=frontcover

[59] http://metapsychology.mentalhelp.net/poc/view_doc.php?type=book&id=557

Adult attention deficit hyperactivity disorder

Adult attention deficit hyperactivity disorder (also referred to as Adult ADHD, Adult ADD, or AADD) is the common term used to describe the neuropsychiatric condition → attention-deficit hyperactivity disorder (ADHD) when it is present in adults. Current convention refers to this condition as adult ADHD, according to the Diagnostic & Statistical Manual for Mental Disorders (DSM-IV-TR), 2000 revision. It has been estimated that 5% of the global population has ADHD (including cases not yet diagnosed).[1]

Up to half of children diagnosed with ADHD as young children continue to demonstrate notable ADHD symptoms into adolescence and young adulthood.[2]

Successful treatment of ADHD is usually based on a combination of medication, behavior therapy, cognitive therapy, and skills training.[3]

Classification

The → DSM-IV, or Diagnostic and Statistical Manual of Mental Disorders, 2000 edition, defines three types of ADHD:

1) An → *inattentive* type

2) A *hyperactive/impulsive* type

3) A *combined* type

In order to meet the formal diagnostic criteria of ADHD, an individual must display:

at least six inattentive-type symptoms for the inattentive-type

at least six hyperactive-type symptoms for the hyperactive/impulsive type

all of the above to have the combined-type

The symptoms (see below) need to have been present since before the individual was 7 years old, and must have interfered with at least two spheres of his or her functioning (at home and at school/work, for example) over the last 6 months.

Signs and symptoms

Individuals with ADHD essentially have problems with self-regulation and self-motivation, predominantly due to problems with distractibility, procrastination, organization, and prioritization. The learning potential and overall intelligence of an adult with ADHD, however, are no different from the potential and intelligence of adults who do not have the disorder. ADHD is a chronic condition, beginning in early childhood and persisting throughout a person's lifetime. It is estimated that up to 70% of children with ADHD will continue to have significant ADHD-related symptoms persisting into adulthood, resulting in a significant impact on education, employment, and interpersonal relationships.

Whereas teachers and caregivers responsible for children are often attuned to the symptoms of ADHD, employers and others who interact with adults are far less likely to regard such behaviors as a symptom. In part, this is because symptoms do change with maturity; adults who have ADHD are less likely to exhibit obvious hyperactive behaviors. Research shows that adults with ADHD are more likely than their non-ADHD counterparts to experience automobile accidents and less likely to complete their education. Their significantly lower rates of professional employment are present, even controlling for confounding psychiatric problems.[4]

Adults with ADHD are often perceived by others as chaotic and disorganized, with a tendency to require high stimulation in order to diminish distractibility and function effectively. As their coping mechanisms become overwhelmed, some individuals may turn to smoking, alcohol, or illicit drugs. As a result, many adults suffer from associated or "co-morbid" psychiatric conditions such as depression, anxiety, or substance abuse.[5] Many with ADHD also have associated learning disabilities, such as dyslexia, which contributes to their difficulties.

Many adults with ADHD are aware that "something is wrong," but are unable to find effective solutions for their symptoms. Getting a formal diagnosis of ADHD by a trained professional (usually a Licensed Professional Counselor, psychiatrist, psychologist, or general practitioner) and understanding the disorder as it applies to them, frequently offer adults with ADHD the insight about their own behaviors that they need in order to make changes. Associated conditions also require treatment.

Inattentive-type (ADHD-I)	Hyperactive/Impulsive-type (ADHD-H)
In **children**:	In **children**:
• Forgetful during daily activities • Easily distracted by extraneous stimuli • Losing important items (e.g. pencils, homework, toys, etc.) • Not listening and not responding to name being called out • Unable to focus on tasks at hand, cannot sustain attention in activities • Avoids or dislikes tasks requiring sustained mental effort • Makes careless mistakes by failing to pay attention to details • Difficulty organizing tasks and activities • Fails to follow-through on complex instructions and tasks (e.g. homework, chores, etc.)	• Squirms and fidgets (with hands and/or feet) • Cannot sit still • Cannot play quietly or engage in leisurely activities • Talks excessively • Runs and climbs excessively • Always on the go, as if "driven by a motor" • Cannot wait for their turn • Blurts out answers • Intrudes on others and interrupts conversations
In **adults**, these evolve into:[6]	In **adults**:
• Procrastination • Indecision, difficulty recalling and organizing details required for a task • Poor time management, losing track of time • Avoiding tasks or jobs that require sustained attention • Difficulty initiating tasks • Difficulty completing and following through on tasks • Difficulty multitasking • Difficulty shifting attention from one task to another	• Chooses highly active, stimulating jobs • Avoids situations with low physical activity or sedentary work • May choose to work long hours or two jobs • Seeks constant activity • Easily bored • Impatient • Intolerant to frustration, easily irritated • Impulsive, snap decisions and irresponsible behaviors • Loses temper easily, angers quickly

Most adults with ADHD have the inattentive-type, but men exhibit a tendency towards the hyperactive/impulsive-type symptoms and have predominantly the combined-type. Symptoms of ADHD can vary widely between individuals and throughout the lifetime of an individual. As the neurobiology of ADHD is becoming increasingly understood, it is becoming evident that difficulties exhibited by individuals with ADHD are due to problems with the brain known as executive functioning (see below, neurobiology). These result in problems with sustaining attention, planning, organizing, prioritizing, and impulsive thinking/decision making. These symptoms are independent of an individual's overall intelligence.

The difficulties generated by these symptoms can range from moderate to extreme. Inability to effectively structure their lives, plan simple daily tasks, or think of consequences results in various difficulties: poor performance in school & work leading to academic underachievement or getting fired, poor driving record with traffic violations and accidents, multiple relationships or marriages, legal problems, STDs, unplanned pregnancies, smoking, alcoholism, substance abuse. As problems accumulate, a negativistic self-view becomes established and a vicious circle of failure is set up. Up to 80% of adults may have some form of psychiatric comorbidity.[7] The difficulty is often due to the ADHD person's observed behaviour (e.g. the impulsive types, who may insult their boss for instance, resulting in dismissal), despite genuinely trying to avoid these and knowing that it can get them in trouble. Often, the ADHD person will miss things that an adult of similar age and experience should catch onto or know. These lapses can lead others to label the individuals with ADHD as "lazy" or "stupid" or "inconsiderate".

Ultimately, this constellation of symptoms can be summarized as a deficiency in self-regulation and self-motivation, especially for the impulsive/hyperactive types. Assessment of adult patients seeking a possible diagnosis can be better than in children due to the adult's greater ability to provide their own history, input, and insight. However, it has been noted that many individuals, particularly those with high intelligence, develop coping strategies that mask ADHD impairments and therefore they do not present for diagnosis and treatment.[8]

Diagnosis

The diagnosis of ADHD in adults is entirely a clinical one, which contributes to controversy. It requires retrospectively establishing whether the symptoms were also present in childhood, even if not previously recognized. There is no objective "test" that diagnoses ADHD. Rather, it is a combination of a careful history of symptoms up to early childhood, including corroborating evidence from family members, previous report cards, etc. along with a neuropsychiatric evaluation. The neuropsychiatric evaluation often includes a battery of tests to assess overall intelligence and general knowledge, self-reported ADHD symptoms, ADHD symptoms reported by others, and tests to screen for co-morbid conditions. Some of these include, but are not limited to the WAIS, BADDS [9], and/or WURS [10] tests in order to have some objective evidence of ADHD.

The screening tests also seek to rule out other conditions or differential diagnoses such as depression, anxiety, or substance abuse. "Organic" diseases such as hyperthyroidism may also present with symptoms similar to those of ADHD, and it is imperative to rule these out as well. Asperger syndrome, a condition on the autism spectrum, is sometimes mistaken for ADHD, due to impairments in executive functioning found in some people with Asperger syndrome. However, Asperger syndrome also typically involves difficulties in social interaction, restricted and repetitive patterns of behavior and interests, and problems with sensory integration, including hypersensitivity.

Generally, medical and mental health professionals follow the → Diagnostic and Statistical Manual of Mental Disorders (DSM) of the American Psychiatric Association. Periodic updates to the DSM incorporate changes in knowledge and treatments.[11] Under the DSM-IV (published in 1994, with corrections and minor changes in 2000), the diagnostic criteria for ADHD in adults follow the same as in children. Many professionals have speculated that in the next DSM (tentatively DSM-V), ADHD in adults may be differentiated from the syndrome as it occurs in children.

It should be noted that every normal individual exhibits ADHD-like symptoms occasionally (when tired or stressed, for example) but in order to have the diagnosis, the symptoms should be present from childhood and persistently interfere with functioning in multiple spheres of an individual's life - work, school, and interpersonal relationships. The symptoms that individuals exhibit as children are still present in adulthood, but manifest differently as most adults develop some form of compensatory mechanisms in order to adapt to their particular environment.

Pathophysiology

Over the last 10 years, research into ADHD has greatly accelerated. There is no single, unified theory that explains the cause of ADHD and research is ongoing.

It is becoming increasingly accepted that individuals with ADHD have difficulty with what neuropsychologists term "executive functioning". In higher organisms, such as humans, these functions are thought to reside in the frontal lobes. They enable us to recall tasks that need accomplishing, organize ourselves to accomplish these tasks, assess the consequences of actions, prioritize thoughts and actions, keep track of time, be aware of our interaction with our surroundings, sort out competing stimuli, and adapt to changing situations. They also enable us to judge what is "right" or "correct" as opposed to what is "wrong" or "incorrect".

(Phineas Gage, a railroad worker who in 1848 survived a large iron rod being accidentally driven through his head, is often cited as a demonstration that executive function resides in the frontal lobes, because at least one of those lobes was destroyed in Gage by the accident, after which his behavior and personality were markedly changed. However, while Gage's case certainly stimulated 19th-century thinking about the brain and the localization of its functions, most specific uses of Gage to illustrate theoretical ideas about the brain employ greatly exaggerated descriptions of his behavioral changes.)[12]

The executive functions of the brain in the frontal lobes are thought to be linked to the rest of the brain by way of the prefrontal cortex. This part of the brain is involved in working memory and linked to the limbic system, which controls our basic emotions of fear, anger, pleasure and also plays an important role in the formation of long-term memories. The nucleus accumbens is a part of the brain that is involved in our internal reward system and allows us to feel pleasure, success, or accomplishments in response to certain stimuli. Many of these interconnections are via dopaminergic pathways. For example, cocaine and amphetamines act directly on this part of the brain to stimulate dopamine release, giving users a euphoric feeling.

Several lines of research based on structural and/or functional imaging techniques, stimulant drugs, psychological interventions have identified alterations in the dopaminergic and adrenergic pathways of individuals with ADHD. In particular, areas of the prefrontal cortex appear to be the most affected. Dopamine and norepinephrine are neurotransmitters playing an important role in brain function. The uptake transporters for dopamine and norepinephrine are overly active and clear these neurotransmitters from the synapse a lot faster than in normal individuals. This is thought to increase processing latency, diminishes working memory, and affects salience. To make an analogy, individuals with ADHD have a problem with the search engine of their brain—the "raw" data (knowledge) is all stored in the cortex, but accessing it, prioritizing it, synthesizing it, and keeping it all in mind is problematic.

Stimulants, such as methylphenidate and amphetamine act on these neurons to increase the availability of dopamine and norepinephrine for neurotransmission. They act to correct the problem with the "wiring". Methylphenidate acts by blocking the dopamine and norepinephrine transporters, thus slowing the pace at which these neurotransmitters are cleared from the synapse. Amphetamine acts in a similar fashion, but also increases the release of these neurotransmitters into the synaptic cleft by temporarily reversing the uptake process. So where Methylphenidate works by "blocking the drain," Amphetamine works by flipping the switch from "suck" to "blow."

Treatment

Stimulant medication is an effective treatment[13] for Adult ADHD [14] [15] although the response rate may be lower for adults than children.[16] Atomoxetine is an effective treatment for adult ADHD without the abuse potential of stimulant medication[17] but has been associated with increased incidence of suicidal thoughts.[18] Some physicians may recommend antidepressant drugs instead of stimulants[19] , though antidepressants have lower treatment effect sizes than stimulant medication.[20]

Treatment for adult ADHD may combine medication and behavioural, cognitive, or vocational interventions. Treatment often begins with medication selected to address the symptoms of ADHD, along with any comorbid conditions that may be present. Medication alone, while effective in correcting the physiological symptoms of ADHD, will not address the paucity of skills which many adults will have failed to acquire because of their ADHD (e.g., one might regain *ability* to focus with medication, but skills such as organizing, prioritizing and effectively communicating have taken others time to cultivate).

Psychosocial therapy

Treatment of adult ADHD may also include forms of stress or anxiety management.

Research has shown that, alongside medication, brief psychological interventions in adults can be effective in reducing symptomatic deficiencies.[21] Although cognitive behavioral therapy has not proven effective in children with ADHD, it may be helpful in adults.[4]

Medications

Stimulant medications are often the 1st line treatment and are usually effective in ~80% of individuals.[22] When stimulants are prescribed low doses are generally recommended for adults with ADHD. High doses of stimulants offer no additional benefit and increase adverse effects.[23] Stimulants are formulated in short-acting, immediate-acting, or long-acting formulations. There is always abuse potential, especially with the short-acting forms which can potentially be injected or snorted which is why long-acting formulations are recommended. Many of these long-acting formulations prevent them from being injected or snorted. In adults, stimulants may increase the risk of adverse cardiovascular events such as myocardial infarctions (heart attacks) or hypertension (high blood pressure). Judicious use and careful, regular follow-up with a physician are therefore critically important.

Methylphenidate is often the first line therapy. In the short term, methylphenidate is well tolerated however long term safety has not been determined in adults and there are concerns about increases in blood pressure in those treated.[24] Again, careful discussion with the treating physician and good clinical judgment are important to decide on the most appropriate therapy.

Amphetamines and their derivatives are also effective in the treatment of adult ADHD. They not only block the uptake of dopamine and norepinephrine, but increase the release of these from the pre-synaptic neuron. They may have a better side-effect profile than methylphenidate, especially in terms of cardiovascular events, and are potentially better tolerated.[25]

Non-stimulant medication, such as atomoxetine, acts by inhibiting the norepinephrine transporter. It is often prescribed in adults who cannot tolerate the side-effects of amphetamines or methylphenidate. It is also effective and approved by the FDA (Food and Drug Administration). A rare but potentially severe side-effect includes liver damage and increased suicidal ideation. These should be discussed with the prescribing physician.

Epidemiology

In North America and Europe, it is estimated that 3-5% of adults have ADHD, but only about 10% of those have received a formal diagnosis.[26] [27] In the context of the World Health Organization World Mental Health Survey Initiative, researchers screened more than 11,000 people aged 18–44 years in ten countries in the Americas, Europe and the Middle East. On this basis they estimated adult ADHD prevalence to average 3.5% with a range of 1.2% to 7.3%, with lower prevalence in lower-income countries (1.9%) compared with higher-income countries (4.2%). They said that adult ADHD often co-occurs with other disorders and is associated with considerable role disability. Few cases are treated for ADHD, but in many cases treatment is given for the co-occurring disorders.[28]

History

In the 1970s researchers began to realize that the condition now known as ADHD did not always disappear in adolescence, as was once thought. At about the same time, some of the symptoms were also noted in many parents of the children under treatment. The condition was formally recognized as afflicting adults in 1978, often informally called *adult ADD*, since symptoms associated with hyperactivity are generally less pronounced.

Societal Impact

ADHD in adults, as with children, is recognized as an impairment that may constitute a disability under U.S. federal disability nondiscrimination laws, including such laws as the Rehabilitation Act of 1973 and the Americans With Disabilities Act (ADA, 2008 revision), if the disorder substantially limits one or more of an individual's major life activities. For adults whose ADHD does constitute a disability, workplaces have a duty to provide reasonable accommodations, and educational institutions have a duty to provide appropriate academic adjustments or modifications, to help the individual work more efficiently and productively.[29] [30]

In a 2004 study it was estimated that the yearly income discrepancy for adults with ADHD was $10,791 less per year than high school graduate counterparts and $4,334 lower for college graduate counterparts. The study estimates a total loss in productivity in the United States of over $77 billion USD (for comparison, loss estimations for: drug abuse, $58 billion; alcohol abuse, $85 billion; and depression, $43 billion).[31]

Further reading

- Amen, Dr. Daniel G., *Healing ADD: The Breakthrough Program That Allows You to See and Heal the Six Types of ADD*
- Doyle, Dr. Brian B, *Understanding and Treating Adults with Attention Deficit Hyperactivity Disorder*
- Hallowell MD, Edward M., and Ratey, John J., *Driven to Distraction: Recognizing and Coping with Attention Deficit Disorder from Childhood to Adulthood*, 1994. ISBN 0684801280. ISBN 978-0684801285.
- Hallowell MD, Edward M., and Ratey, John J., *Answers to Distraction*, 1995. ISBN 055337821X. ISBN 978-0553378214.
- Hallowell MD, Edward M., and Ratey, John J., *Delivered from Distraction: Getting the Most out of Life with Attention Deficit Disorder*, 2005. ISBN 034544230X. ISBN 978-0345442307.
- Hartmann, Thom, *Attention Deficit Disorder: A New Perspective*
- Kelly, Kate, Peggy Ramundo. (1993) You Mean I'm Not Lazy, Stupid or Crazy?! A Self-Help Book for Adults with Attention deficit Disorder. ISBN 0-684-81531-1
- Ratey, Nancy. (2008) The Disorganized Mind: Coaching Your ADHD Brain to Take Control of Your Time, Tasks, and Talents. ISBN 0312355335
- Weiss, Lynn. (2005) Attention Deficit Disorder in Adults, 4th Edition: A Different Way of Thinking ISBN 1589792378
- Hersey, Jane, *Why Can't My Child Behave?*
- Lawlis, Frank, *The ADD Answer*
- Matlen, Terry. (2005) "Survival Tips for Women with AD/HD". ISBN 1886941599
- Solden, Sari, *Women with Attention Deficit Disorder*
- Solden, Sari, "Journeys Through ADDulthood"
- Mate, Dr. Gabor, "Scattered Minds"
- Brown, Dr Thomas E. "Attention Deficit Disorder: The Unfocused Mind in Children and Adults", Yale University Press, Sep 2005.

External links

- National Institute for Mental Health official website [32]
- National Mental Health association, AADD webpage [33]
- National Attention Deficit Disorder Association [34]
- CHADD [35] Support groups, national education devoted to helping and supporting people with ADD and ADHD
- Living with ADD/ADHD [36]
- ADDults with ADHD (Australian) [37]
- Today Show segment on adult ADHD, June 5, 2008 [38]
- www.aadd.org.uk [39] Adults with Attention Deficit Disorder UK
- ADDitude magazine [40] Adult ADHD Information
- www.lbctnz.co.nz [41] Complete informational guide to add/adhd and dyxlexia. NZ
- ADDA-SR [42] Resource network, support groups, referrals, educational events

References

[1] http://ajp.psychiatryonline.org/cgi/content/abstract/164/6/942

[2] Karande S (December 2005). "Attention deficit hyperactivity disorder--a review for family physicians". *Indian J Med Sci* **59** (12): 546–55. PMID 16385176 (http://www.ncbi.nlm.nih.gov/pubmed/16385176).

[3] You've Got Adult ADD... Now What? (http://www.additudemag.com/adhd/article/815.html), *ADDitude* magazine, 2007

[4] Anthshel, Kevin; Faraone, Steven; Kunwar, Arun (November 2008). " ADHD in Adults: How to Recognize and Treat (http://www.psychiatrictimes.com/adhd/article/10162/1349954)". *Psychiatric Times* **48** (12). .

[5] http://www.psychiatrymmc.com/displayArticle.cfm?articleID=article218

[6] Katragadda S. and Schubiner H. ADHD in Children, Adolescents, and AdultsSreenivas, Prim Care Clin Office Pract 34:317–341, 2007

[7] Katragadda S. and Schubiner H. ADHD in Children, Adolescents, and Adults. Prim Care Clin Office Pract 34:317–341, 2007

[8] http://www.neuropsychiatryreviews.com/feb00/npr_feb00_ADHD.html

[9] http://www.drthomasebrown.com/assess_tools/index.html

[10] http://ajp.psychiatryonline.org/cgi/content/abstract/150/6/885

[11] http://kadi.myweb.uga.edu/The_Development_of_the_DSM.html

[12] Macmillan, M. (2008). " Phineas Gage – Unravelling the myth *The Psychologist* (British Psychological Society), 21(9): 828-831 (http://www.thepsychologist.org.uk/archive/archive_home.cfm?volumeID_21-editionID_164-ArticleID_1399-getfile_getPDF/thepsychologist\0908look.pdf)" (PDF). .

[13] Dusan Kolar, Amanda Keller, Maria Golfinopoulos, Lucy Cumyn, Cassidy Syer, and Lily Hechtman (February 2008). " Treatment of adults with attention-deficit/hyperactivity disorder (http://www.pubmedcentral.nih.gov/articlerender.fcgi?tool=pubmed&pubmedid=18728812)". *Neuropsychiatr Dis Treat* **4** (1): 107–121. PMID 18728812 (http://www.ncbi.nlm.nih.gov/pubmed/18728812). .

[14] Spencer TJ. (April 2007). " Pharmacology of adult ADHD with stimulants. (http://www.cnsspectrums.com/aspx/articledetail.aspx?articleid=1671)". *CNS Spectr* **12** (4(supplement 6)): 8–11. PMID 17715564 (http://www.ncbi.nlm.nih.gov/pubmed/17715564). .

[15] Rostain, Anthony L. (September 2008). " ADHD in Adults: Attention-Deficit/Hyperactivity Disorder in Adults: Evidence-Based Recommendations for Management (http://www.postgradmed.com/index.php?art=pgm_09_2008?article=1905)". *Postgraduate Medicine* **120** (3): 27–38. doi: 10.3810/pgm.2008.09.1905 (http://dx.doi.org/10.3810/pgm.2008.09.1905). PMID 18824823 (http://www.ncbi.nlm.nih.gov/pubmed/18824823). .

[16] Spencer, Thomas. Biederman, Joseph. Wilens, Timothy (June 2004). " Stimulant treatment of adult attention-deficit/hyperactivity disorder (http://www.mdconsult.com/das/article/body/138353191-2/jorg=journal&source=&sp=14616830&sid=0/N/410882/1.html?issn=0193-953X)". *Psychiatric Clinics of North America* **27** (2). .

[17] Simpson D, Plosker GL (2004). "Spotlight on atomoxetine in adults with attention-deficit hyperactivity disorder". *CNS Drugs* **18** (6): 397–401. doi: 10.2165/00023210-200418060-00011 (http://dx.doi.org/10.2165/00023210-200418060-00011). PMID 15089111 (http://www.ncbi.nlm.nih.gov/pubmed/15089111).

[18] http://www.foxnews.com/story/0,2933,170777,00.html

[19] Higgins ES (January 1999). "A comparative analysis of antidepressants and stimulants for the treatment of adults with attention-deficit hyperactivity disorder". *J Fam Pract* **48** (1): 15–20. PMID 9934377 (http://www.ncbi.nlm.nih.gov/pubmed/9934377).

[20] Verbeeck W, Tuinier S, Bekkering GE. (February 2009). " Antidepressants in the treatment of adult attention-deficit hyperactivity disorder: a systematic review. (http://www.springerlink.com/content/ph82718338384515/fulltext.pdf)". *Adv Ther* **26** (2): 170–184. doi: 10.1007/s12325-009-0008-7 (http://dx.doi.org/10.1007/s12325-009-0008-7). PMID 19238340 (http://www.ncbi.nlm.nih.gov/pubmed/19238340). .

[21] Weiss M., et al. Research Forum on Psychological Treatment of Adults With ADHD. J of Att Dis 2008; 11(6) 642-651.http://jad.sagepub.com/cgi/content/abstract/11/6/642

[22] Spencer T, Biederman J, Wilens T, et al. 2005. A large, double-blind, randomized clinical trial of methylphenidate in the treatment of adults with attention deficit/hyperactivity disorder. Biol Psychiatry, 57:456–63.

[23] Sachdev PS, Trollor JN (August 2000). " How high a dose of stimulant medication in adult attention deficit hyperactivity disorder? (http:// www3.interscience.wiley.com/resolve/openurl?genre=article&sid=nlm:pubmed&issn=0004-8674&date=2000&volume=34&issue=4& spage=645)". *Aust N Z J Psychiatry* **34** (4): 645–50. doi: 10.1046/j.1440-1614.2000.00732.x (http://dx.doi.org/10.1046/j.1440-1614. 2000.00732.x). PMID 10954396 (http://www.ncbi.nlm.nih.gov/pubmed/10954396). .

[24] Godfrey J (May 2008). "Safety of therapeutic methylphenidate in adults: a systematic review of the evidence". *J. Psychopharmacol. (Oxford)* **23**: 194. doi: 10.1177/0269881108089809 (http://dx.doi.org/10.1177/0269881108089809). PMID 18515459 (http://www.ncbi. nlm.nih.gov/pubmed/18515459).

[25] Kolar D, et al. Treatment of adults with attention deficit/hyperactivity disorder. Neuropsychiatric Disease and Treatment 2008:4(2)389–403

[26] The prevalence and effects of adult attention-deficit/hyperactivity disorder (ADHD) on the performance of workers: results from the WHO World Mental Health Survey Initiative (http://oem.bmj.com/cgi/content/abstract/65/12/835)

[27] The Prevalence and Correlates of Adult ADHD in the United States: Results From the National Comorbidity Survey Replication (http://ajp. psychiatryonline.org/cgi/content/full/ajp;163/4/716)

[28] Fayyad J., De Graaf R., Kessler R., Alonso J., Angermeyer M., Demyttenaere K., De Girolamo G., Haro J.M., Karam E.G., Lara C., Lepine J.-P., Ormel J., Posada-Villa J., Zaslavsky A.M., Jin R., "Cross-national prevalence and correlates of adult attention-deficit hyperactivity disorder" *British Journal of Psychiatry* 190, May 2007, pp402-409

[29] U.S. Equal Employment Opportunity Commission, Enforcement Guidance: Reasonable Accommodation and Undue Hardship Under the Americans with Disabilities Act (http://www.eeoc.gov/policy/docs/accommodation.html)

[30] U.S. Department of Education, Office of Civil Rights, Questions and Answers on Disability Discrimination under Section 504 and Title II (http://www.ed.gov/about/offices/list/ocr/qa-disability.html)

[31] http://news.healingwell.com/index.php?p=news1&id=521145

[32] http://www.nimh.nih.gov/publicat/adhd.cfm

[33] http://www.nmha.org/go/information/get-info/ad/hd/ad/hd-and-adults

[34] http://www.add.org/

[35] http://www.chadd.org

[36] http://www.livingwithadd.org/

[37] http://www.add.org.au/

[38] http://video.yourtotalhealth.ivillage.com/player/?id=259833&ice=th%7Cvid_tout%7C1

[39] http://www.aadd.org.uk

[40] http://www.additudemag.com/channel/adult-add-adhd/index.html

[41] http://www.lbctnz.co.nz

[42] http://www.adda-sr.org

Auditory processing disorder

Auditory processing disorder	
Classification and external resources	
ICD-9	315.32 [1], 388.45 [2]
MeSH	D001308 [3]

Auditory Processing Disorder (APD) (also known as **(Central) Auditory Processing Disorder** or **(C)APD**) is a disorder in the way auditory information is processed in the brain. It is not a sensory (inner ear) hearing impairment; individuals with APD usually have normal peripheral hearing ability. APD is an umbrella term that describes a variety of problems with the brain that can interfere with processing auditory information.

Definitions

The American Speech-Language-Hearing Association (ASHA) published "(Central) Auditory Processing Disorders" in January 2005 as an update to the "Central Auditory Processing: Current Status of Research and Implications for Clinical Practice (ASHA, 1996)",[4] complementing the UK's Medical Research Council's Institute of Hearing Research's [5] *Auditory Processing Disorder (APD) pamphlet, Oct 2004*.[6]

Auditory processing disorder can be a congenital or an acquired condition (for example; resulting from ear infections and head injuries) which refers to difficulties in the processing of auditory information within the central nervous system, such as problems with: "...sound localization and lateralization; auditory discrimination; auditory pattern recognition; temporal aspects of audition, including temporal integration, temporal discrimination (e.g., temporal gap detection), temporal ordering, and temporal masking; auditory performance in competing acoustic signals (including dichotic listening); and auditory performance with degraded acoustic signals."[7]

It is recommended, and in some areas a legal requirement, that Auditory Processing Disorder is assessed and diagnosed by an audiologist (better still, an assessment team composed of an audiologist, a speech and language Pathologist, and an educational psychologist).[8]

The Committee of UK Medical Professionals Steering the UK Auditory Processing Disorder Research Program have developed the following working definition of Auditory Processing Disorder:

"APD results from impaired neural function and is characterized by poor recognition, discrimination, separation, grouping, localization, or ordering of non-speech sounds. It does not solely result from a deficit in general attention, language or other cognitive processes."[9]

Diagnosis

As APD is one of the more difficult information processing disorders to detect and diagnose, it may sometimes be misdiagnosed as → ADD/ADHD, Asperger syndrome and other forms of autism, but it may also be a comorbid[10] aspect of those conditions if it is considered a significant part of the overall diagnostic picture. APD shares common symptoms in areas of overlap such that professionals who were not aware of APD would diagnose the disabilities as those which they were aware of.

People with APD intermittently experience an inability to process verbal information. When people with APD have a processing failure, they do not process what is being said to them. They may be able to repeat the words back word for word, but the meaning of the message is lost. Simply repeating the instruction is of no use if a person with APD is not processing. Neither will increasing the volume help.

People with APD have a disorder processing auditory information *within* the brain. The written word is a visual notation of verbal language, thus Auditory Processing Disorder can extend into reading and writing.

There are also many other hidden implications, which are not always apparent even to the person with the disability. For example, because people with APD are used to guessing to fill in the processing gaps, they may not even be aware that they have misunderstood something.

APD has been defined anatomically in terms of the integrity of the auditory nervous system[11], as "what we do with what we hear",[12] and in terms of performances on a selected group of behavioral auditory tests (Task Force for the American Speech, Language, and Hearing Association; ASHA, 1994). The ASHA Task Force definition considered APD to be any observed deficits in one or more of these so-called "behaviors". Problems inherent in test validation by consensus are highlighted by the succession of task force reports that have appeared in recent years. The first of these occurred in 1996.[4] This was followed by a conference organized by the American Academy of Audiology[13] that explicitly embraced modality specificity as a defining characteristic of auditory processing disorders. Subsequently, an ASHA committee rejected modality specificity as a defining characteristic of auditory processing disorders.[14]

There have been several commentaries questioning various aspects of these proposals.[12] [15] [16] Additionally, Moore suggests that APD is primarily a difficulty in processing non-speech sounds and that a population-based approach should be taken to identify outlying performers.[16] However, inclusive conceptualizations of APD have been criticized based on their lack of diagnostic specificity.[17] [18] Auditory processing disorder has been defined as a modality specific perceptual dysfunction that is not due to peripheral hearing loss.[15] [19] This viewpoint emphasizes the perceptual nature of auditory processing and asserts that the disorder should be conceptualized as being limited to problems in processing auditory material. Numerous authors have suggested that existing tests of APD may be sensitive to factors that are not of an auditory perceptual nature.[20] [21] Modality specificity has been advocated as a way to improve APD diagnosis.[15] [19]

Causes

The causes of APD are unknown. There is anecdotal evidence to suggest links to autistic spectrum disorder, middle ear infections and lack of oxygen at birth, among other conditions.

Characteristics

Persons with APD often:

- have trouble paying attention to and remembering information presented orally; they cope better with visually acquired information
- may have trouble paying attention and remembering information when information is simultaneously presented in multiple modalities
- have problems carrying out multi-step directions given orally; need to hear only one direction at a time
- appear to have poor listening skills, and need people to speak slowly
- need more time to process information.
- develop a dislike for locations with background noise such as bar, clubs or other social locations
- prefer written communication (e.g. text chat)
- have behavioral problems.

APD can manifest as problems determining the direction of sounds, difficulty perceiving differences between speech sounds and the sequencing of these sounds into meaningful words, confusing similar sounds such as "hat" with "bat", "there" with "where", etc. Fewer words may be perceived than were actually said, as there can be problems detecting the gaps between words, creating the sense that someone is speaking unfamiliar or nonsense words. Those suffering from APD may have problems relating what has been said with its meaning, despite obvious recognition that a word has been said, as well as repetition of the word. Background noise, such as the sound of a radio, television or a noisy bar can make it difficult to impossible to understand speech, depending on the severity of the auditory processing disorder. Using a telephone can be problematic for someone with auditory processing disorder, in comparison with someone with normal auditory processing, due to low quality audio, poor signal, intermittent sounds and the chopping of words.[14] Many who have auditory processing disorder subconsciously develop visual coping strategies, such as lip reading, reading body language, and eye contact, to compensate for their auditory deficit, and these coping strategies are not available when using a telephone.

Secondary characteristics

Those who have APD tend to be quiet or shy, even withdrawn from mainstream society due to their communication problems, and the lack of understanding of these problems by their peers.

One who fails to process any part of the communication of others may be unable to comprehend what is being communicated. This has some obvious social and educational implication, which can cause a lack of understanding from others. In adults this can lead to persistent interpersonal relationship problems.

Some of these signs can be shared with other related disorders which can also have areas of overlap, such as acquired brain injury, attention deficits, dyslexia or learning difficulties, hearing loss, and psychologically-based behavioral problems.

APD may be related to cluttering,[22] a fluency disorder marked by word and phrase repetitions.

Remediations and training

There are no research supported treatments for APD available, however a variety of treatments have been offered commercially despite the absence of empirical research in support of their efficacy.

- Auditory Integration Training typically involves a child attending two 30-minute sessions per day for ten days.[23]
- Lindamood-Bell Learning Processes (particularly, the Visualizing and Verbalizing program)
- Physical activities which require frequent crossing of the midline (e.g. occupational therapy)
- Sound Field Amplification

Relation to Specific language impairment

APD can also be confused with Specific language impairment (SLI).

SLI is more specifically a problem associated with the linking of words, both written and spoken, to semantics (meaning) and someone can have both APD and SLI. Unlike those with SLI, those with APD can usually get the meaning of language from written words where those with SLI show problems with both heard and read words, demonstrating that the basic issue is not an auditory one.

Those with APD have auditory difficulty distinguishing sounds including speech from extraneous sounds, e.g. fans or other chatter. APD is purely about processing what you hear both verbal and non-verbal. For those who have APD, difficulty processing verbal language is only one of many symptoms.

See also

- Asperger syndrome
- Attention-Deficit Hyperactivity Disorder
- King-Kopetzky syndrome (now included in the UK Medical Research Councils definition of APD)
- Pure word deafness

External links

- American Speech-Language-Hearing Association (ASHA) [24]
- UK Medical Research Council Institute of Hearing Research) [5]
- Auditory Processing Disorder in the Uk (APDUK) [25]
- Support community for CAPD [26]

References

[1] http://www.icd9data.com/getICD9Code.ashx?icd9=315.32

[2] http://www.icd9data.com/getICD9Code.ashx?icd9=388.45

[3] http://www.nlm.nih.gov/cgi/mesh/2009/MB_cgi?field=uid&term=D001308

[4] " Central Auditory Processing: Current Status of Research and Implications for Clinical Practice. Technical Report, (1996) (http://www.asha.org/docs/html/TR1996-00241.html)". *Working Group on Auditory Processing Disorders.* American Speech-Language-Hearing Association. .

[5] http://www.ihr.mrc.ac.uk/research/apd.php/

[6] " Auditory Processing Disorder (APD). Pamphlet, (2004). (http://www.ihr.mrc.ac.uk/research/apd.php/apd.php?page=apd_docs)". *British Society of Audiology APD Special Interest Group.* MRC Institute of Hearing Research. . Retrieved 2008-01-15.

[7] (Central) Auditory Processing Disorders, Technical Report, Jan 2005)

[8] http://www.infolinks.apduk.org/international_page.htm from where you can still download a copy of Arkansas Department of Education GUIDELINES FOR DETERMINING A CENTRAL AUDITORY PROCESSING DISORDER

[9] http://www.thebsa.org.uk/apd/Home.htm The British Society of Audiology and the UK APD Steering Group

[10] http://www.tsbvi.edu/Outreach/seehear/spring00/centralauditory.htm

[11] Rintelmann, W.F. (1985). Monaural speech tests in the detection of central auditory disorders. In M.L. Pinheiro, & F.E. Musiek (Eds.), Assessment of central auditory dysfunction: foundations and clinical correlates (pp. 173-200). Baltimore: Williams & Wilkens

[12] Katz, J. (1992). Classification of auditory processing disorders. In J. Katz, N. Stecker, D. Henderson (Eds.), Central Auditory Processing: A Transdisciplinary View (p. 81-92). Chicago: Mosby Yearbook.

[13] Jerger, J, Musiek, F (2000) Report of the Consensus Conference in the diagnosis of auditory processing disorders in school-aged children. Journal of the American Academy of Audiology, 11, 467-474.

[14] " (Central) Auditory Processing Disorders. Technical Report, (2005). (http://www.asha.org/docs/html/TR2005-00043.html)". *Working Group on Auditory Processing Disorders..* American Speech-Language-Hearing Association... .

[15] Cacace, AT and McFarland, DJ (2005) The importance of modality specificity in diagnosing central auditory processing disorder. *American Journal of Audiology,* 14: 112-123.

[16] Moore DR (2006). Auditory processing disorder (APD): Definition, diagnosis, neural basis, and intervention. Audiological Medicine, 4, p4-11

[17] Rees, N.: Auditory processing factors in language disorders: The view from Procrustes' bed. Journal of Speech and Hearing Disorders, 1973, 38, 304–315

[18] Cacace A T; McFarland D J, Central auditory processing disorder in school-aged children: a critical review. Journal of speech, language, and hearing research : JSLHR 1998;41(2):355-73.

[19] Cacace, Anthony T., McFarland, Dennis J. Opening Pandora's Box: The Reliability of CAPD Tests Am J Audiol 1995 4: 61-62

[20] Friel-Patti, S. (1999) Clinical decision-making in the assessment and intervention of central auditory processing disorders. "Language, Speech, and Hearing Services in the Schools", 30, 345-352

[21] Grundast, K.M, Berkowiitz, R.G, Connerss, C.K.,and Bellman, P. (191) Complete evaluation of the child identified as a poor listener. "International Journal of Pediatric Otorhinolarynglogy", 21, 65-78.

[22] William O. Haynes, Rebekah Hand Pindzola, Michael J. Moran, Communication Disorders in the Classroom: An Introduction for Professionals in School Settings, ISBN 0763727431, Jones & Bartlett Publishers (2006), p. 251

[23] Mudford OC, Cullen C (2004). "Auditory integration training: a critical review". in Jacobson JW, Foxx RM, Mulick JA (eds.). *Controversial Therapies for Developmental Disabilities.* Routledge. pp. 351–62. ISBN 080584192X.

[24] http://search.asha.org/default.aspx?q=auditory+processing+disorder

[25] http://www.apduk.org/

[26] http://www.capdsupport.org

Chemical imbalance

Chemical imbalance is one theory about the cause of mental illness. Other causes that are debated include psychological and social causes.

The basic concept is that neurotransmitter imbalances within the brain are the main causes of psychiatric conditions and that these conditions can be improved with medication which corrects these imbalance. The phrase originated from the scientific study of brain chemistry. In the 1950s the monoamine oxidase inhibitors (MAOIs) and tricyclic antidepressants were accidentally discovered to be effective in the treatment of depression[1] . These findings and other supporting evidence led Joseph Schildkraut to publish his paper called "The Catecholamine Hypothesis of Affective Disorders" in 1965.[2] Schildkraut associated low levels of neurotransmitters with depression.

Research into other mental illnesses such as schizophrenia also found that too little activity of certain neurotransmitters was correlated to these disorders. In the scientific community this hypothesis has been referred to as the **Monoamine Hypothesis**. This hypothesis has been a major focus of research in the fields Pathophysiology and Pharmacotherapy for over 25 years [3] and led to the development of new classes of drugs such as SSRIs (selective-serotonin reuptake inhibitors)[4] . This conceptual framework has been challenged within the scientific community, though no other demonstrably superior hypothesis has emerged. While the hypothesis has been shown to be simplistic and lacking, there is sufficient evidence to consider it as a useful heuristic in the aiding of our understanding of brain chemistry and explaining pharmacotherapy.[3] [5] Wayne Goodman, Chair of the U.S. Food and Drug Administration It may be noted, for example, that, while the most commonly prescribed medications for depression increase the availability of only one to three neurotransmitters, science has so far identified over 100 existing neurotransmitters in the human body. Manipulation of serotonin, norepinephrine and dopamine availability may fall far short of truly treating the larger picture of depression as a systemic disease. Psychopharmacological Advisory Committee, has described the serotonergic theory of depression as a "useful metaphor" for understanding depression, though not one that he uses with his own psychiatric patients.[6] Recently, psychiatrist Peter Kramer stated that the serotonin theory of depression had been declared dead prematurely.[7] Kramer argues that recent scientific research actually shows a definitive role for serotonin deficiency in depression. An analysis of the studies Kramer cites argues that such statements are premature.[8]

Monoamine hypothesis

Monoamine Hypothesis is a biological theory stating that depression is caused by the underactivity in the brain of monoamines, such as dopamine, serotonin, and norepinephrine.

In the 1950s the monoamine oxidase inhibitors (MAOIs) and tricyclic antidepressants were accidentally discovered to be effective in the treatment of depression.[1] These findings and other supporting evidence led Joseph Schildkraut to publish his paper called "The Catecholamine Hypothesis of Affective Disorders" in 1965.[2] Schildkraut associated low levels of neurotransmitters with depression. Research into other mental impairments such as schizophrenia also found that too little activity of certain neurotransmitters were connected to these disorders.

The hypothesis has been a major focus of research in the fields pathophysiology and pharmacotherapy for over 25 years.[3] and led to the development of new classes of drugs such as SSRIs (selective serotonin reuptake inhibitors).[4]

Dopamine hypothesis

In studying the causes of schizophrenia, particular focus has been placed upon the function of dopamine in the mesolimbic pathway of the brain. This focus largely resulted from the accidental finding that a drug group which blocks dopamine function, known as the phenothiazines, could reduce psychotic symptoms. It is also supported by the fact that amphetamines, which triggers the release of dopamine may exacerbate the psychotic symptoms in schizophrenia.[9] An influential theory, known as the Dopamine hypothesis of schizophrenia, proposed that a malfunction involving dopamine pathways was the cause of (the positive symptoms of) schizophrenia. This theory is now thought to be overly simplistic as a complete explanation, partly because newer antipsychotic medication (called atypical antipsychotic medication) can be equally effective as older medication (called typical antipsychotic medication), but also affects serotonin function and may have slightly less of a dopamine blocking effect.[10]

Criticisms

According to critics, the chemical imbalance hypothesis has been overpromoted and continues to be advanced as factual by pharmaceutical companies. They believe the general population and many journalists have accepted this hypothesis into their understanding of mental illness uncritically.[11] They have pointed to the lack of an established chemical *balance* (without which, they claim, the notion of an "imbalance" is meaningless). Certain pharmaceutical companies such as Pfizer continue to promote drugs like Zoloft with advertisements asserting that mental illness *may* be due to chemical imbalances in the brain, and that their drugs work to "correct" this imbalance. [12] Most academics believe that the advertisements are oversimplified and don't fully explain what is happening. [13]

Chemical imbalances theories do not presume individual laboratory tests be obtained from a patient at the time of prescription, such as one would expect in the analogy to physical medicine. For example, someone suffering from schizophrenia is not given haloperidol on the basis of a laboratory test which shows that his or her dopamine level is too high.

Chemical imbalances theories distinguish, between 'side' and 'main' drug effects in recording the response to the drug. 'Side' effects are considered to be simple, direct, predictible, allowable effects which are merely 'physical' but do include often flattened affect and memory, emotive and cognitive effects. These drug effects may then be cited capriciously as further evidence to confirm the diagnosis as correct, confusing cause and effect.

When 'improvement' is measured in industry research studies, attention is given only to the 'main' effect - typically a complex, indirect, interpersonal, perceptual, cultural change, thereby confusing cause with coincidence. There does not exist in chemical imbalance theories, effectiveness measures using standard social networks and associated tests before and after drugs administration.

Chemical imbalance theories predominate in 'streamline' public sector medicine for lower social class and homeless persons, where drugs constitute the only form of treatment. There is much wishful thinking in attribution of drug effect, particularly in cases like schizophrenia, where there no longer exists a patient [non-drug user] control group available.

See also

- BDNF

References

[1] Drugs and the Brain: Antidepressants (http://www.csusm.edu/DandB/AD.html)

[2] The catecholamine hypothesis of affective disorders: a review of supporting evidence. 1965 [classical article] - Schildkraut 7 (4): 524 - J Neuropsychiatry Clin Neurosci (http://neuro.psychiatryonline.org/cgi/content/citation/7/4/524)

[3] Looking Beyond the Monoamine Hypothesis (http://www.touchneurology.com/looking-beyond-monoamine-hypothesis-a5616-1.html)

[4] Mental Illness - GSU Biology 4102 / 6102 (http://bio4102.homeip.net/labwiki/index.php/Mental_Illness)

[5] The Catecholamine Hypothesis of Affective Disorders: A review of Supporting Evidence - Schildkraut 122 (5): 509 - Am J Psychiatry (http://ajp.psychiatryonline.org/cgi/content/abstract/122/5/509)

[6] Television adverts for antidepressants cause anxiety (http://www.newscientist.com/article/mg18825252.500.html), from *New Scientist*. Published November 12 2005; accessed November 17 2007.

[7] http://blogs.psychologytoday.com/blog/in-practice/200804/the-chemical-imbalance-theory-dead-or-alive The "Chemical Imbalance" Theory: Dead or Alive?

[8] http://chemicalimbalance.org/?p=6 Is Clinical Depression Caused by a Serotonin Imbalance? A Response to Peter Kramer.

[9] Laruelle M; Abi-Dargham A, van Dyck CH, Gil R, D'Souza CD, Erdos J, McCance E, Rosenblatt W, Fingado C, Zoghbi SS, Baldwin RM, Seibyl JP, Krystal JH, Charney DS, Innis RB (1996). "Single photon emission computerized tomography imaging of amphetamine-induced dopamine release in drug-free schizophrenic subjects". *Proceedings of the National Academy of Sciences of the USA* **93**: 9235–40. doi: 10.1073/pnas.93.17.9235 (http://dx.doi.org/10.1073/pnas.93.17.9235). PMID 8799184 (http://www.ncbi.nlm.nih.gov/pubmed/8799184).

[10] Jones HM; Pilowsky LS (2002). "Dopamine and antipsychotic drug action revisited". *British Journal of Psychiatry* **181**: 271–275. doi: 10.1192/bjp.181.4.271 (http://dx.doi.org/10.1192/bjp.181.4.271). PMID 12356650 (http://www.ncbi.nlm.nih.gov/pubmed/12356650).

[11] The Media and the Chemical Imbalance Theory of Depression (http://www.springerlink.com/content/u37j12152n826q60/fulltext.pdf)

[12] http://medicine.plosjournals.org/archive/1549-1676/2/12/pdf/10.1371_journal.pmed.0020392-L.pdf Serotonin and depression: a disconnect between the advertisements and the scientific literature. Lacasse JR, Leo J. PLoS Medicine. 2005 Dec;2(12):e392.

[13] " Advertisements for SSRIs may be misleading (http://www.medscape.com/viewarticle/516262)". .

Educational psychology

Educational psychology is the study of how humans learn in educational settings, the effectiveness of educational interventions, the psychology of teaching, and the social psychology of schools as organizations. Educational psychology is concerned with how students learn and develop, often focusing on subgroups such as gifted children and those subject to specific disabilities. Although the terms "educational psychology" and "school psychology" are often used interchangeably, researchers and theorists are likely to be identified in the US and Canada as educational psychologists, whereas practitioners in schools or school-related settings are identified as school psychologists. This distinction is however not made in the UK, where the generic term for practitioners is "educational psychologist."

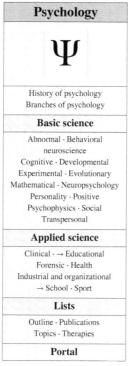

Psychology
Ψ
History of psychology Branches of psychology
Basic science
Abnormal · Behavioral neuroscience Cognitive · Developmental Experimental · Evolutionary Mathematical · Neuropsychology Personality · Positive Psychophysics · Social Transpersonal
Applied science
Clinical · → Educational Forensic · Health Industrial and organizational → School · Sport
Lists
Outline · Publications Topics · Therapies
Portal

Educational psychology can in part be understood through its relationship with other disciplines. It is informed primarily by psychology, bearing a relationship to that discipline analogous to the relationship between medicine and biology. Educational psychology in turn informs a wide range of specialities within educational studies, including instructional design, educational technology, curriculum development, organizational learning, special education and classroom management. Educational psychology both draws from and contributes to cognitive science and the learning sciences. In universities, departments of educational psychology are usually housed within faculties of education, possibly accounting for the lack of representation of educational psychology content in introductory psychology textbooks.[1]

Social, moral and cognitive development

To understand the characteristics of learners in childhood, adolescence, adulthood, and old age, educational psychology develops and applies theories of human development. Often represented as stages through which people pass as they mature, developmental theories describe changes in mental abilities (cognition), social roles, moral reasoning, and beliefs about the nature of knowledge.

An abacus provides concrete experiences for learning abstract concepts.

For example, educational psychologists have researched the instructional applicability of Jean Piaget's theory of development, according to which children mature through four stages of cognitive capability. Piaget hypothesized that children are not capable of abstract logical thought until they are older than about 11 years, and therefore younger children need to be taught using concrete objects and examples. Researchers have found that transitions, such as from concrete to abstract logical thought, do not occur at the same time in all domains. A child may be able to think abstractly about mathematics, but remain limited to concrete thought when reasoning about human relationships. Perhaps Piaget's most enduring contribution is his insight that people actively construct their understanding through a self-regulatory process.[2]

Piaget proposed a developmental theory of moral reasoning in which children progress from a naive understanding of morality based on behavior and outcomes to a more advanced understanding based on intentions. Piaget's views of moral development were elaborated by Kohlberg into a stage theory of moral development. There is evidence that the moral reasoning described in stage theories is not sufficient to account for moral behavior. For example, other factors such as modeling (as described by the social cognitive theory of morality) are required to explain bullying.

Rudolf Steiner's model of child development interrelates physical, emotional, cognitive, and moral development[3] in developmental stages similar to those later described by Piaget.[4]

Developmental theories are sometimes presented not as shifts between qualitatively different stages, but as gradual increments on separate dimensions. Development of epistemological beliefs (beliefs about knowledge) have been described in terms of gradual changes in people's belief in: certainty and permanence of knowledge, fixedness of ability, and credibility of authorities such as teachers and experts. People develop more sophisticated beliefs about knowledge as they gain in education and maturity.[5]

Individual differences and disabilities

Each person has an individual profile of characteristics, abilities and challenges that result from learning and development. These manifest as individual differences in intelligence, creativity, cognitive style, motivation, and the capacity to process information, communicate, and relate to others. The most prevalent disabilities found among school age children are → attention-deficit hyperactivity disorder (ADHD), learning disability, dyslexia, and speech disorder. Less common disabilities include mental retardation, hearing impairment, cerebral palsy, epilepsy, and blindness.[2]

Choose the figure that completes the series.

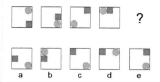

An example of an item from a cognitive abilities test.

Although theories of intelligence have been discussed by philosophers since Plato, intelligence testing is an invention of educational psychology, and is coincident with the development of that discipline. Continuing debates about the nature of intelligence revolve on whether intelligence can be characterized by a single factor known as general intelligence,[6] multiple factors (e.g., Gardner's theory of multiple intelligences[7]), or whether it can be measured at all. In practice, standardized instruments such as the Stanford-Binet IQ test and the WISC[8] are widely used in economically developed countries to identify children in need of individualized educational treatment. Children classified as gifted are often provided with accelerated or enriched programs. Children with identified deficits may be provided with enhanced education in specific skills such as phonological awareness.

Learning and cognition

Two fundamental assumptions that underlie formal education systems are that students (a) retain knowledge and skills they acquire in school, and (b) can apply them in situations outside the classroom. But are these assumptions accurate? Research has found that, even when students report not using the knowledge acquired in school, a considerable portion is retained for many years and long term retention is strongly dependent on the initial level of mastery.[9] One study found that university students who took a child development course and attained high grades showed, when tested 10 years later, average retention scores of about 30%, whereas those who obtained moderate or lower grades showed average retention scores of about 20%.[10] There is much less consensus on the crucial question of how much knowledge acquired in school transfers to tasks encountered outside formal educational settings, and how such transfer occurs.[11] Some psychologists claim that research evidence for this type of *far transfer* is scarce,[12] [13] while others claim there is abundant evidence of far transfer in specific domains.[14] Several perspectives have been established within which the theories of learning used in educational psychology are formed and contested. These include behaviorism, cognitivism, social cognitive theory, and constructivism. This section summarizes how educational psychology has researched and applied theories within each of these perspectives.

Behavioral perspective

Applied behavior analysis, a set of techniques based on the behavioral principles of operant conditioning, is effective in a range of educational settings.[15] For example, teachers can improve student behavior by systematically rewarding students who follow classroom rules with praise, stars, or tokens exchangeable for sundry items.[16] [17] Despite the demonstrated efficacy of awards in changing behavior, their use in education has been criticized by proponents of self-determination theory, who claim that praise and other rewards undermine intrinsic motivation. There is evidence that tangible rewards decrease intrinsic motivation in specific situations, such as when the student already has a high level of intrinsic motivation to perform the goal behavior.[18] But the results showing detrimental effects are counterbalanced by evidence that, in other situations, such as when rewards are given for attaining a gradually increasing standard of performance, rewards enhance intrinsic motivation.[19] [20] Many effective therapies have been based on the principles of Applied Behavior Analysis, including Pivotal Response Therapy which is used to treat Autism Spectrum Disorders.

Cognitive perspective

Among current educational psychologists, the cognitive perspective is more widely held than the behavioral perspective perhaps because it admits causally related mental constructs such as traits, beliefs, memories, motivations and emotions. Cognitive theories claim that memory structures determine how information is perceived, processed, stored, retrieved and forgotten. Among the memory structures theorized by cognitive psychologists are separate but linked visual and verbal systems described by Allan Paivio's dual coding theory. Educational psychologists have used dual coding theory and cognitive load theory to explain how people learn from multimedia presentations.[21]

The spaced learning effect, a cognitive phenomenon strongly supported by psychological research, has broad applicability within education.[23] For example, students have been found to perform better on a test of knowledge about a text passage when a second reading of the passage is delayed rather than immediate (see figure).[22] Educational psychology research has confirmed the applicability to education of other findings from cognitive psychology, such as the benefits of using mnemonics for immediate and delayed retention of information.[24]

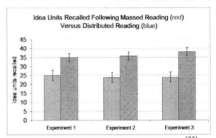

Three experiments reported by Krug, Davis and Glover[22] demonstrated the advantage of delaying a 2nd reading of a text passage by one week (distributed) compared with no delay between readings (massed).

Problem solving, regarded by many cognitive psychologists as fundamental to learning, is an important research topic in educational psychology. A student is thought to interpret a problem by assigning it to a schema retrieved from long term memory. When the problem is assigned to the wrong schema, the student's attention is subsequently directed away from features of the problem that are inconsistent with the assigned schema.[25] The critical step of finding a mapping between the problem and a pre-existing schema is often cited as supporting the centrality of analogical thinking to problem solving.

Social cognitive perspective

Social cognitive theory is a highly influential fusion of behavioral, cognitive and social elements that was initially developed by educational psychologist Albert Bandura. In its earlier, neo-behavioral incarnation called *social learning theory*, Bandura emphasized the process of observational learning in which a learner's behavior changes as a result of observing others' behavior and its consequences. The theory identified several factors that determine whether observing a model will affect behavioral or cognitive change. These factors include the learner's developmental status, the perceived prestige and competence of the model, the consequences received by the model, the relevance of the model's behaviors and consequences to the learner's goals, and the learner's self-efficacy. The concept of self-efficacy, which played an important role in later developments of the theory, refers to the learner's belief in his or her ability to perform the modeled behavior.

An experiment by Schunk and Hanson,[26] that studied grade 2 students who had previously experienced difficulty in learning subtraction, illustrates the type of research stimulated by social learning theory. One group of students observed a subtraction demonstration by a teacher and then participated in an instructional program on subtraction. A second group observed other grade 2 students performing the same subtraction procedures and then participated in the same instructional program. The students who observed peer models scored higher on a subtraction post-test and also reported greater confidence in their subtraction ability. The results were interpreted as supporting the hypothesis that perceived similarity of the model to the learner increases self-efficacy, leading to more effective learning of modeled behavior. It is supposed that peer modeling is particularly effective for students who have low self-efficacy.

Over the last decade, much research activity in educational psychology has focused on developing theories of self-regulated learning (SRL) and metacognition. These theories work from the central premise that effective learners are active agents who construct knowledge by setting goals, analysing tasks, planning strategies and monitoring their understanding. Research has indicated that learners who are better at goal setting and self-monitoring tend to have greater intrinsic task interest and self-efficacy;[27] and that teaching learning strategies can increase academic achievement.[28]

Constructivist perspective

Constructivism is a category of learning theories in which emphasis is placed on the agency and prior knowledge of the learner, and often on the social and cultural determinants of the learning process. Educational psychologists distinguish individual (or psychological) constructivism, identified with Piaget's learning theory, from social constructivism. A dominant influence on the latter type is Lev Vygotsky's work on sociocultural learning, describing how interactions with adults, more capable peers, and cognitive tools are internalized to form mental constructs. Elaborating on Vygotsky's theory, Jerome Bruner and other educational psychologists developed the important concept of instructional scaffolding, in which the social or information environment offers supports for learning that are gradually withdrawn as they become internalized.

Motivation

Motivation is an internal state that activates, guides and sustains behavior. Educational psychology research on motivation is concerned with the volition or will that students bring to a task, their level of interest and intrinsic motivation, the personally held goals that guide their behavior, and their belief about the causes of their success or failure.

A form of attribution theory developed by Bernard Weiner[29] describes how students' beliefs about the causes of academic success or failure affect their emotions and motivations. For example, when students attribute failure to lack of ability, and ability is perceived as uncontrollable, they experience the emotions of shame and embarrassment and consequently decrease effort and show poorer performance. In contrast, when students attribute failure to lack of effort, and effort is perceived as controllable, they experience the emotion of guilt and consequently increase effort and show improved performance.

Motivational theories also explain how learners' goals affect the way that they engage with academic tasks.[30] Those who have *mastery goals* strive to increase their ability and knowledge. Those who have *performance approach goals* strive for high grades and seek opportunities to demonstrate their abilities. Those who have *performance avoidance* goals are driven by fear of failure and avoid situations where their abilities are exposed. Research has found that mastery goals are associated with many positive outcomes such as persistence in the face of failure, preference for challenging tasks, creativity and intrinsic motivation. Performance avoidance goals are associated with negative outcomes such as poor concentration while studying, disorganized studying, less self-regulation, shallow information processing and test anxiety. Performance approach goals are associated with positive outcomes, and some negative outcomes such as an unwillingness to seek help and shallow information processing.

Research methodology

The research methods used in educational psychology tend to be drawn from psychology and other social sciences. There is also a history of significant methodological innovation by educational psychologists, and psychologists investigating educational problems. Research methods address problems in both research design and data analysis. Research design informs the planning of experiments and observational studies to ensure that their results have internal, external and ecological validity. Data analysis encompasses methods for processing both quantitive (numerical) and qualitative (non-numerical) research data. Although, historically, the use of quantitative methods was often considered an essential mark of scholarship, modern educational psychology research uses both quantitative and qualitative methods.

Quantitative methods

Perhaps first among the important methodological innovations of educational psychology was the development and application of factor analysis by Charles Spearman. Factor analysis is mentioned here as one example of the many multivariate statistical methods used by educational psychologists. Factor analysis is used to summarize relationships among a large set of variables or test questions, develop theories about mental constructs such as self-efficacy or anxiety, and assess the reliability and validity of test scores.[31] Over one hundred years after its introduction by Spearman, factor analysis has become a research staple figuring prominently in educational psychology journals.

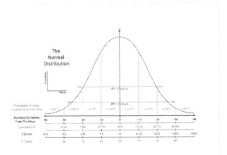

Test scores and other educational variables often approximate a normal distribution.

Because educational assessment is fundamental to most quantitative research in the field, educational psychologists have made significant contributions to the field of psychometrics. For example, alpha, the widely used measure of test reliability was developed by educational psychologist Lee Cronbach. The reliability of assessments are routinely reported in quantitative educational research. Although, originally, educational measurement methods were built on classical test theory, item response theory and Rasch models are now used extensively in educational measurement worldwide. These models afford advantages over classical test theory, including the capacity to produce standard errors of measurement for each score or pattern of scores on assessments and the capacity to handle missing responses.

Meta-analysis, the combination of individual research results to produce a quantitative literature review, is another methodological innovation with a close association to educational psychology. In a meta-analysis, effect sizes that represent, for example, the differences between treatment groups in a set of similar experiments, are averaged to obtain a single aggregate value representing the best estimate of the effect of treatment.[32] Several decades after Pearson's work with early versions of meta-analysis, Glass[33] published the first application of modern meta-analytic techniques and triggered their broad application across the social and biomedical sciences. Today, meta-analysis is among the most common types of literature review found in educational psychology research.

Other quantitative research issues associated with educational psychology include the use of nested research designs (e.g., a student nested within a classroom, which is nested within a school, which is nested within a district, etc.) and the use of longitudinal statistical models to measure change.

Qualitative methods

Qualitative methods are used in educational studies whose purpose is to describe events, processes and situations of theoretical significance. The qualitative methods used in educational psychology often derive from anthropology, sociology or sociolinguistics. For example, the anthropological method of ethnography has been used to describe teaching and learning in classrooms. In studies of this type, the researcher may gather detailed field notes as a participant observer or passive observer. Later, the notes and other data may be categorized and interpreted by methods such as grounded theory. Triangulation, the practice of cross-checking findings with multiple data sources, is highly valued in qualitative research.

Case studies are forms of qualitative research focusing on a single person, organization, event, or other entity. In one case study,[34] researchers conducted a 150-minute, semi-structured interview with a 20-year old woman who had a history of suicidal thinking between the ages of 14 to 18. They analyzed an audio-recording of the interview to understand the roles of cognitive development, identity formation and social attachment in ending her suicidal thinking.

Qualitative analysis is most often applied to verbal data from sources such as conversations, interviews, focus groups, and personal journals. Qualitative methods are thus, typically, approaches to gathering, processing and reporting verbal data. One of the most commonly used methods for qualitative research in educational psychology is protocol analysis.[35] In this method the research participant is asked to *think aloud* while performing a task, such as solving a math problem. In protocol analysis the verbal data is thought to indicate which information the subject is attending to, but is explicitly not interpreted as an explanation or justification for behavior. In contrast, the method of verbal analysis[36] does admit learners' explanations as a way to reveal their mental model or misconceptions (e.g., of the laws of motion). The most fundamental operations in both protocol and verbal analysis are segmenting (isolating) and categorizing sections of verbal data. Conversation analysis and discourse analysis, sociolinguistic methods that focus more specifically on the structure of conversational interchange (e.g., between a teacher and student), have been used to assess the process of conceptual change in science learning.[37] Qualitative methods are also used to analyse information in a variety of media, such as students' drawings and concept maps, video-recorded interactions, and computer log records.

Applications in instructional design and technology

Instructional design, the systematic design of materials, activities and interactive environments for learning, is broadly informed by educational psychology theories and research. For example, in defining learning goals or objectives, instructional designers often use a taxonomy of educational objectives created by Benjamin Bloom and colleagues.[38] Bloom also researched mastery learning, an instructional strategy in which learners only advance to a new learning objective after they have mastered its prerequisite objectives. Bloom[39] discovered that a combination of mastery learning with one-to-one tutoring is highly effective, producing learning outcomes far exceeding those normally achieved in classroom instruction. Gagné, another psychologist, had earlier developed an influential method of task analysis in which a terminal

Bloom's taxonomy of educational objectives: categories in the cognitive domain[38]

learning goal is expanded into a hierarchy of learning objectives[40] connected by prerequisite relations.

- Intelligent tutoring system
- Educational technology
- John R. Anderson
- Cognitive tutor
- Cooperative learning
- Collaborative learning
- problem-based learning
- Computer supported collaborative learning
- William Winn
- constructive alignment

Applications in teaching

Research on classroom management and pedagogy is conducted to guide teaching practice and form a foundation for teacher education programs. The goals of classroom management are to create an environment conducive to learning and to develop students' self-management skills. More specifically, classroom management strives to create positive teacher-student and peer relationships, manage student groups to sustain on-task behavior, and use counselling and other psychological methods to aid students who present persistent psychosocial problems.[42]

Introductory educational psychology is a commonly required area of study in most North American teacher education programs. When taught in that context, its content varies, but it typically emphasizes learning theories (especially cognitively oriented ones), issues about motivation, assessment of students' learning, and classroom management. A developing Wikibook about

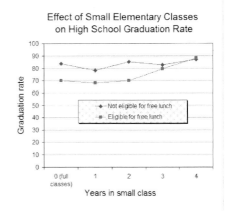

Effect of Small Elementary Classes on High School Graduation Rate

A class size experiment in the United States found that attending small classes for 3 or more years in the early grades increased high school graduation of students from low income families.[41]

educational psychology gives more detail about the educational psychology topics that are typically presented in preservice teacher education.

- Special education
- Lesson plan
- More about applications to classroom teaching

History

Educational psychology cannot claim priority in the systematic analysis of educational processes. Philosophers of education such as Democritus, Quintilian, Vives and Comenius, had examined, classified and judged the methods of education centuries before the beginnings of psychology in the late 1800s. Instead, aspirations of the new discipline rested on the application of the scientific methods of observation and experimentation to educational problems. Even in the earliest years of the discipline, educational psychologists recognized the limitations of this new approach. In his famous series of lectures *Talks to Teachers on Psychology*, published in 1899 and now regarded as the first educational psychology textbook, the pioneering American psychologist William James commented that:

“ Psychology is a science, and teaching is an art; and sciences never generate arts directly out of themselves. An intermediate inventive mind ” ”
must make that application, by using its originality.[43]

According to Berliner[44] educational psychology theorists' attitude to the world of educational practice has shifted
from initial interest to disdain, and eventually to respect.

• Charles Hubbard Judd

In 1912, Thorndike, who developed the theory of instrumental conditioning, presaged later work on programmed
instruction, mastery learning and computer-based learning:

“ If, by a miracle of mechanical ingenuity, a book could be so arranged that only to him who had done what was directed on page one would ” ”
page two become visible, and so on, much that now requires personal instruction could be managed by print.[45]

Among the few works of educational psychology historiography is *Educational Psychology: A Century of
Contributions*[46] which presents chapter-length biographies of 16 eminent scholars whose work has significantly
influenced the development of educational psychology.

Careers in educational psychology

Education and training

A person may be considered an educational psychologist after completing a graduate degree in educational
psychology or a closely related field. Universities establish educational psychology graduate programs in either
psychology departments or, more commonly, faculties of education.

Educational psychologists work in a variety of settings. Some work in university settings where they carry out
research on the cognitive and social processes of human development, learning and education. Educational
psychologists may also work as consultants in designing and creating educational materials, classroom programs and
online courses.

Educational psychologists who work in k-12 school settings (called → school psychologists in the United States) are
trained at the masters and doctoral levels. In addition to conducting assessments, school psychologists provide
services such as academic and behavioral intervention, counseling, teacher consultation, and crisis intervention.

In the UK, status as a *Chartered Educational Psychologist* is gained by completing:

• an undergraduate degree in psychology permitting registration with the British Psychological Society
• two or three years experience working with children, young people and their families.
• a three-year professional doctorate in educational psychology.

The previous requirement to train and work for two years as a teacher has now been abandoned.

Employment outlook

Employment for psychologists in the United States is expected to grow faster than most occupations through the year
2014, with anticipated growth of 18-26%. One in four psychologist are employed in educational settings. In the
United States, the median salary for psychologists in primary and secondary schools is $58,360 as of May 2004.[47]

In recent decades the participation of women as professional researchers in North American educational psychology
has risen dramatically.[48] The percentage of female authors of peer-reviewed journal articles doubled from 1976
(24%) to 1995 (51%), and has since remained constant. Female membership on educational psychology journal
editorial boards increased from 17% in 1976 to 47% in 2004. Over the same period, the proportion of chief editor
positions held by women increased from 22% to 70%.

Research journals

There are several peer-reviewed research journals in educational psychology tracked by Journal Citation Reports. The most highly cited journals related to educational psychology are currently *Child Development* and *Educational Psychologist*.

See also

- List of educational psychologists
- Applied psychology
- Articles related to educational psychology
- American Educational Research Association
- American Psychological Association
- Association for Psychological Science
- British Psychological Society
- Educational psychologists
- Contemporary Educational Psychology
- Educational research
- Evolutionary educational psychology
- Important publications in educational psychology
- International Society of the Learning Sciences
- Learning sciences
- List of education topics
- Sociology of education
- Philosophy of education
- School psychologist

External links

- Educational Psychology Resources [49] by Athabasca University
- Division 15 of the American Psychological Association [50]
- Educational Psychology Interactive [51]
- Psychology of Education Section of the British Psychological Society [52]
- School Psychology on the Web [53]
- Explorations in Learning & Instruction: The Theory Into Practice Database [54]
- Classics in the History of Psychology [55]
- The Standards for Educational and Psychological Testing [56]
- EPNET - Educational Psychology forum [57]

Careers

- United Kingdom description of educational psychologist [58]
- Educational Psychologist description from the British Psychological Society [59]
- Careers in Educational Psychology [60]

Textbooks

- Psychology Applied To Teaching [61] by Jack Snowman and Robert Biehler
- Educational Psychology [62] by John Santrock
- Educational Psychology [63] by Robert Slavin
- Educational Psychology: Developing Learners [64] by Jeanne Ormrod
- Educational Psychology [65] by Anita Woolfolk
- Educational Psychology: Effective Teaching, Effective Learning [66] by Elliot, Kratochwill, Cook & Travers
- Educational Psychology [67], by Kelvin Seifert and Rosemary Sutton (online)

References

[1] Lucas, J. L., Blazek, M. A., & Raley, A. B. (2005). The lack of representation of educational psychology and school psychology in introductory psychology textbooks. *Educational Psychology, 25*, 347-351.

[2] Woolfolk, A. E.,Winne,P. H. & Perry, N. E. (2006). Educational Psychology (3rd Canadian ed.). Toronto, Canada: Pearson.

[3] Woods, Ashley and Woods, *Steiner Schools in England*, University of West of England, Bristol: Research Report RR645 (http://www.dfes. gov.uk/research/data/uploadfiles/RR645.pdf), section 1.5, "Findings from the survey and case studies"

[4] Carrie Y. Nordlund, "Art Experiences in Waldorf Education", Ph.D. Dissertation, University of Missouri-Columbia, May 2006

[5] Cano, F. (2005). Epistemological beliefs and approaches to learning: Their change through secondary school and their influence on academic performance. *British Journal of Educational Psychology, 75*, 203-221.

[6] Spearman, C. (1904). "General intelligence" objectively determined and measured. "American Journal of Psychology", 15, 201–293.

[7] Gardner, Howard. (1983) "Frames of Mind: The Theory of Multiple Intelligences." New York: Basic Books.

[8] Wechsler, D. (1949). *The Wechsler Intelligence Scale for Children*. New York: Psychological Corp.

[9] Semb, G. B., & Ellis, J. A. (1994). Knowledge taught in schools: What is remembered? *Review of Educational Research, 64*, 253-286.

[10] Ellis, J. A., Semb, G. B., & Cole, B. (1998). Very long-term memory for information taught in school. *Contemporary Educational Psychology, 23*, 419-433.

[11] Perkins, D. N., & Salomon, G. (1992). Transfer of learning (http://learnweb.harvard.edu/alps/thinking/docs/traencyn.htm). *International Encyclopedia of Education* (2nd ed.). Oxford, UK: Pergamon Press.

[12] Perkins, D. N., & Grotzer, T. A. (1997). Teaching intelligence. *American Psychologist, 52*, 1125-1133.

[13] Detterman, D. K. (1993). The case for the prosecution: Transfer as an epiphenomenon. In D. K. Detterman & R. J. Sternberg (Eds.), *Transfer on trial: Intelligence, cognition, and instruction* (pp. 1-24). Norwood, NJ: Ablex.

[14] Halpern, D. F. (1998). Teaching critical thinking for transfer across domains. *American Psychologist, 53*, 449-455.

[15] Alberto, P., & Troutman, A. (2003). Applied behavior analysis for teachers (6th ed.). Columbus, OH, USA: Prentice-Hall-Merrill.

[16] McGoey, K. E., & DuPaul, G. J. (2000). Token reinforcement and response cost procedures: Reducing the disruptive behavior of preschool children with attention-deficit/hyperactivity disorder. *School Psychology Quarterly, 15*, 330-343.

[17] Theodore, L. A., Bray, M. A., Kehle, T. J., & Jenson, W. R. (2001). Randomization of group contingencies and reinforcers to reduce classroom disruptive behavior. *Journal of School Psychology, 39*, 267-277.

[18] Lepper, M. R., Greene, D. & Nisbett, R. E. (1973). Undermining children's intrinsic interest with extrinsic reward: A test of the "overjustification" hypothesis. *Journal of Personality and Social Psychology, 28*, 129-137.

[19] Cameron, J., Pierce, W. D., Banko, K. M., & Gear, A. (2005). Achievement-based rewards and intrinsic motivation: A test of cognitive mediators. *Journal of Educational Psychology, 97*, 641-655.

[20] Pierce, W. D. & Cameron, J. (2002). A summary of the effects of reward contingencies on interest and performance. *The Behavior Analyst Today*, 3, 222-226.

[21] Mayer, R. E. (2001). Multimedia learning. Cambridge, UK: Cambridge University Press.

[22] Krug, D., Davis, T. B., Glover, J. A. (1990). Massed versus distributed repeated reading: A case of forgetting helping recall? *Journal of Educational Psychology, 82*, 366-371.

[23] Dempster, F. N. (1989). Spacing effects and their implications for theory and practice. *Educational Psychology Review, 1*, 309-330.

[24] Carney, R. N., & Levin, J. R. (2000). Fading mnemonic memories: Here's looking anew, again! *Contemporary Educational Psychology, 25*, 499-508.

[25] Kalyuga, S., Chandler, P., Tuovinen, J., & Sweller, J. (2001). When problem solving is superior to studying worked examples. *Journal of Educational Psychology, 93*, 579-588.

[26] Schunk, D. H., & Hanson, A. R. (1985). Peer models: Influence on children's self-efficacy and achievement behavior. *Journal of Educational Psychology, 77*, 313-322.

[27] Zimmerman, B. J. (1998). Developing self-fulfilling cycles of academic regulation: An analysis of exemplary instructional models. In D. H. Schunk & B. J. Zimmerman (Eds.) *Self-regulated learning: From teaching to self-reflective practice (pp. 1-19). New York: Guilford.*

[28] Hattie, J., Biggs, J., & Purdie, N. (1996). Effects of learning skills interventions on student learning: A meta-analysis. *Review of Educational Research, 66*, 99-136.

[29] Weiner, B. (2000). Interpersonal and intrapersonal theories of motivation from an attributional perspective. *Educational Psychology Review, 12*, 1-14.

[30] Elliot, A. J. (1999). Approach and avoidance motivation and achievement goals. *Educational Psychologist, 34*, 169–189.

[31] Thompson, B. (2004). *Exploratory and confirmatory factor analysis: Understanding concepts and applications.* Washington, DC, USA: American Psychological Association.

[32] Lipsey, M. W., & Wilson, D. B. (2001). *Practical meta-analysis.* London: Sage.

[33] Glass, G. V. (1976). Primary, secondary, and meta-analysis of research. *Educational Researcher, 5*, 3-8.

[34] Everall, R. D., Bostik, K. E. & Paulson, B. L. (2005). I'm sick of being me: Developmental themes in a suicidal adolescent. *Adolescence, 40*, 693-708.

[35] Ericsson, K. A., & Simon, H. (1993). *Protocol analysis: Verbal reports as data* (Rev. ed.). Cambridge, MA: MIT Press.

[36] Chi, M. T. H. (1997). Quantifying qualitative analyses of verbal data: A practical guide. *Journal of the Learning Sciences, 6*, 271-315.

[37] Pea, R. D. (1993). Learning scientific concepts through material and social activities: Conversational analysis meets conceptual change. *Educational Psychologist, 28*, 265-277.

[38] Anderson, L. W., & Krathwohl, D. R. (2001). *A taxonomy for learning, teaching, and assessing: A revision of Bloom's taxonomy of educational objectives.* New York, USA: Addison-Wesley Longman.

[39] Bloom, B. S. (1984). The two sigma problem: The search for methods of group instruction as effective as one-to-one tutoring. *Educational Researcher, 13*(6),4–16.

[40] Gronlund, N. E. (2000). *How to write and use instructional objectives* (6th ed.). Columbus, OH, USA: Merrill.

[41] Finn, J. D., Gerber, S. B., Boyd-Zaharias, J. (2005). Small classes in the early grades, academic achievement, and graduating from high school. *Journal of Educational Psychology, 97*, 214-233.

[42] Emmer, E. T., & Stough, L. M. (2001). Classroom management: A critical part of educational psychology with implications for teacher education. *Educational Psychologist, 36*, 103-112.

[43] James, W. (1983). *Talks to teachers on psychology and to students on some of life's ideals.* Cambridge, MA: Harvard University Press. (Original work published 1899)

[44] Berliner, D. C. (1993). The 100-year journey of educational psychology: From interest to disdain to respect for practice (http://courses.ed.asu.edu/berliner/readings//journey.htm). In T. K. Fagan & G. R. VandenBos (Eds) *Exploring applied psychology: Origins and critical analysis.* Washington DC: American Psychology Association.

[45] Thorndike, E. L. (1912). *Education: A first book.* New York: MacMillan.

[46] Zimmerman, B. J., & Schunk, D. H. (Eds.)(2003). *Educational psychology: A century of contributions.* Mahwah, NJ, US: Erlbaum.

[47] Bureau of Labor Statistics, U.S. Department of Labor. *Occupational Outlook Handbook.* 2006-07 Edition. Psychologists. retrieved from http://www.bls.gov/oco/ocos056.htm on June 30, 2006.

[48] Evans, J., Hsieh, P. P., & Robinson, D. H. (2005). Women's Involvement in educational psychology journals from 1976 to 2004. *Educational Psychology Review, 17*, 263-271.

[49] http://psych.athabascau.ca/html/aupr/educational.shtml

[50] http://www.apa.org/about/division/div15.html

[51] http://teach.valdosta.edu/whuitt/index.html

[52] http://www.bps.org.uk/education/education_home.cfm

[53] http://www.schoolpsychology.net/

[54] http://tip.psychology.org/index.html

[55] http://psychclassics.yorku.ca/index.htm

[56] http://www.apa.org/science/standards.html

[57] http://www.jiscmail.ac.uk/lists/epnet.html

[58] http://www.prospects.ac.uk/cms/ShowPage/Home_page/Explore_types_of_jobs/Types_of_Job/p!eipaL?state=showocc&pageno=1&idno=67

[59] http://www.bps.org.uk/careers/areas/educational.cfm

[60] http://www.wcupa.edu/_ACADEMICS/sch_cas.psy/Career_Paths/Educational/Career04.htm

[61] http://www.hmco.com/education/snowman/psych_app/10e/students/index.html

[62] http://www.mhhe.com/socscience/education/santrock2e/santrock_bridge.html

[63] http://www.abacon.com/slavin/index.html

[64] http://www.prenhall.com/ormrod/ormrod-presell/index1.html

[65] http://wps.ablongman.com/ab_woolfolk_edpsych_9

[66] http://www.mhhe.com/socscience/education/elliott/

[67] http://docs.globaltext.terry.uga.edu:8095/anonymous/webdav/Educational%20Psychology/Educational%20Psychology.pdf

School psychology

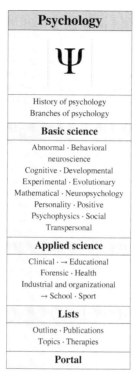

Psychology
Ψ
History of psychology Branches of psychology
Basic science
Abnormal · Behavioral neuroscience Cognitive · Developmental Experimental · Evolutionary Mathematical · Neuropsychology Personality · Positive Psychophysics · Social Transpersonal
Applied science
Clinical · → Educational Forensic · Health Industrial and organizational → School · Sport
Lists
Outline · Publications Topics · Therapies
Portal

School psychology is a field that applies principles of clinical psychology and → educational psychology to the diagnosis and treatment of children's and adolescents' behavioral and learning problems. School psychologists are educated in psychology, child and adolescent development, child and adolescent psychopathology, education, family and parenting practices, learning theories, and personality theories. They are knowledgeable about effective instruction and effective schools. They are trained to carry out psychological and psychoeducational assessment, psychotherapy, and consultation, and in the ethical, legal and administrative codes of their profession.

Education

Unlike clinical psychology and counseling psychology, which are doctoral-only fields, school psychology includes individuals with Master's (M.A., M.S., M.Ed.), Educational Specialist (Ed.S.), Certificate of Advanced Graduate Studies (C.A.G.S.) and doctoral (Ph.D., Psy.D. or Ed.D) degrees. Whereas in the past the Master's degree was considered appropriate for practice in schools, the National Association of School Psychologists currently recognizes the 60 credit hour Ed.S. as the most appropriate level of training needed for entry-level school-based practice. According to the NASP Research Committee (NASP Research Committee, 2007), in 2004-05, 33% of school psychologists possessed Master's degrees, 35% the Educational Specialist (Ed.S.) degree, and 32% doctoral (Ph.D., Psy.D., or Ed.D.) degrees.

Most school psychology training programs are housed in university schools of education. School psychology programs require courses, practica, and internships that cover the domains of

1. Data-based decision-making and accountability;
2. Consultation and collaboration;
3. Effective instruction and development of cognitive/academic skills;
4. Socialization and development of life skills;
5. Student diversity in development and learning;
6. School and systems organization, policy development, and climate;
7. Prevention, crisis intervention, and mental health;
8. Home / school / community collaboration;
9. Research and program evaluation;
10. School psychology practice and development; and
11. Information technology Standards for Training and Field Placement, 2007. Specialist-level training typically requires 3–4 years of graduate training including a 9-month (1200 hour) internship in a school setting. Doctoral-level training programs typically require 5–7 years of graduate training including a 12-month internship (1500+ hours), which may be in a school or other (e.g., medical) setting. Doctoral level training differs from [specialist degree|specialist]-level training in that it requires students to take more coursework in core psychology and professional psychology. In addition, doctoral programs typically require students to learn more advanced statistics, to be involved in research endeavors, and to complete a doctoral dissertation constituting original research APA Committee on Accreditation, 2008;with

Doctoral training programs may be approved by NASP and/or accredited by the American Psychological Association. In 2007, approximately 125 programs were approved by NASP, and 58 programs were accredited by APA. Another 11 APA-accredited programs were combined (clinical/counseling/school, clinical/school, or counseling/school) programs (American Psychological Association, 2007). A list of school psychology graduate programs at all levels across the U.S. can be found at the University of California Berkeley's website [1].

School psychology services

School psychologists are experts in both psychology and education. School psychologists address the educational, emotional, social, and behavioral challenges that many children, youth, and young adults experience. They apply their understanding of human development, psychopathology, the impact of culture, learning theory, the principles of effective instruction and effective schools, and the impact of parent and family functioning on children to serve learners and their families. As noted by the National Association of School Psychologists (NASP, 2007) and the American Psychological Association (APA, 2007), school psychologists adhere to the scientist-practitioner framework and make decisions based on empirical research.

Although school psychologists understand that schools are important in the lives of young people, not all school psychologists are employed in schools. Many school psychologists, particularly those with doctoral degrees, practice in other settings, including clinics, hospitals, forensic settings, correctional facilities, universities, and independent practice (ABPP, n.d.).

In many states school psychologists with terminal Master's or Education Specialist degrees are limited to employment in school settings. School psychologists employed in schools conduct psychological and educational assessments, provide interventions, and develop and present prevention programs for individuals from birth to age 21. They consult with teachers, other psychological and school personnel, family physicians and psychiatrists, and other professionals about students and are actively involved in district and school crisis intervention teams. They also may provide professional development to teachers and other school personnel on topics such as positive behavior intervention plans and AD/HD and carry out individual, group, and family counseling.

Employment prospects in school psychology

The job prospects in school psychology in the U.S. are excellent. The U.S. Department of Labor cites employment opportunities in school psychology at both the specialist and doctoral levels as among the best across all fields of psychology (U.S. Dept. of Labor, 2006-07).

According to the NASP Research Committee (2007), 74% of school psychologists are female with an average age of 46. In 2004-05, average earnings for school practitioners ranged from $56,262 for those with a 180-day annual contract to $68,764 for school psychologists with a 220-day contract.

Journals and other publications related to school psychology

* Journal of School Psychology [2]
* School Psychology International [3]
* Psychology in the Schools [4]
* The School Psychologist [5]
* Journal of Psychoeducational Assessment [6]
* School Psychology Quarterly [7]
* School Psychology Review [8]
* School Psychology Forum: Research in Practice [9]
* NASP Communiqué [10]

See also

* Applied psychology
* Educational Psychology
* School Counselor
* School Psychological Examiner
* School Social Worker
* Special Education

References

* American Board of Professional Psychology (n.d.). Specialty certification in school psychology. Brochure retrieved on January 31, 2008 from American Board of Professional Psychology. [11]
* American Psychological Association (2007). Accredited internship and postdoctoral programs for training in psychology: 2007. American Psychologist, Vol 62(9), December 2007. pp. 1016-1040.
* American Psychological Association Commission for the Recognition of Specialties and Proficiencies in Professional Psychology (n.d.). Archival description of school psychology. Retrieved on December 29, 2007 from American Psychological Association [12]
* Committee on Accreditation (January 1, 2008). Guidelines and principles for accreditation of programs in professional psychology. Washington D.C.: APA. Retrieved on June 6, 2007 from, American Psychological Association. [13]
* Fagan, T. K. (1996). Witmer's contributions to school psychological services. American Psychologist, 51.
* Fagan, T. K. & Wise, P. S. (2007). School Psychology: Past, present, and future, (3rd ed.). Bethesda, MD: National Association of School Psychologists.
* Merrell, K. W., Ervin, R. A., & Gimpel, G. A. (2006). School psychology for the 21st century. NY: Guilford.
* National Association of School Psychologists (July 15, 2000). Standards for Training and Field Placement Programs in School Psychology / Standards for the Credentialing of School Psychologists. National Association of School Psychologists. [14]

- National Association of School Psychologists (2007). A Career in School Psychology: Selecting a Master's, Specialist, or Doctoral Degree Program That Meets Your Needs. Bethesda, MD: NASP. Retrieved on June 4, 2007 from National Association of School Psychologists. [15]
- National Association of School Psychologists Research Committee (2007). Demographics of the profession of school psychology. Retrieved on December 29, 2007 from University of California, Santa Barbara. [16]
- United States Department of Labor Occupational Outlook Handbook (OOH), 2006-2007 Edition. U.S. Bureau of Labor Statistics [17]

External links

- American Psychological Association [18]
  - Division 16-School Psychology [19]
  - The Standards for Educational and Psychological Testing [56]
- International School Psychology Association [20]
- National Association of School Psychologists [21]
- School Psychology Resources [53]
- Global School Psychology Network [22]

Outline of psychology

References

[1] http://www-gse.berkeley.edu/program/SP/html/sp_gradprograms.html
[2] http://www.sciencedirect.com/science/journal/00224405
[3] http://spi.sagepub.com/
[4] http://www3.interscience.wiley.com/cgi-bin/jhome/32084
[5] http://www.indiana.edu/~div16/psychologist.htm
[6] http://jpa.sagepub.com/
[7] http://www.indiana.edu/~div16/quarterly.htm
[8] http://www.nasponline.org/publications/spr/sprmain.aspx
[9] http://www.nasponline.org/publications/spf/index.aspx
[10] http://www.nasponline.org/publications/cq/cqmain.aspx
[11] http://www.abpp.org/
[12] http://www.apa.org/crsppp/schpsych.html
[13] http://www.apa.org/ed/accreditation/coalist.html
[14] http://www.nasponline.org/standards/index.aspx
[15] http://www.nasponline.org/students/degreefactsheet.pdf
[16] http://education.ucsb.edu/netshare/cdspp/midwinter.html
[17] http://www.bls.gov/oco/ocos056.htm
[18] http://www.apa.org
[19] http://www.apa.org/about/division/div16.html
[20] http://www.ispaweb.org
[21] http://www.nasponline.org
[22] http://www.globalschoolpsychology.net/

Sensory integration dysfunction

Sensory integration dysfunction is a term used to describe difficulty with sensory integration. The more current diagnostic nosology (Miller et al., 2007) uses the term Sensory Processing Disorder to describe this condition.

As a symptom

Along with *sensory processing dysfunction*, the term *sensory integration dysfunction* is used informally in the medical literature to describe any such difficulty. Various conditions can involve sensory integration dysfunction, such as schizophrenia,[1] [2] [3] succinic semialdehyde dehydrogenase deficiency,[4] primary nocturnal enuresis,[5] prenatal alcohol exposure,[6] and autism,[7] [8] [9] as well as people with traumatic brain injury[10] or who have had cochlear implants placed.[11]

As a discrete disorder

The concept of sensory integration dysfunction as a discrete disorder was popularized by Anna Jean Ayres, an occupational therapist. Today, some occupational therapists argue in favor of creating a discrete diagnostic category for sensory integration dysfunction, but this position is disputed.[12] [13] SID is not a recognized diagnosis in the → DSM-IV-TR or the ICD-10.

See also

- Autism
- Hypokalemic sensory overstimulation
- Sensory defensiveness
- Sensory integration therapy
- Sensory overload

References

[1] Ross, A.; Saint-Amour, D.; Leavitt, M.; Molholm, S.; Javitt, C.; Foxe, J. (Dec 2007). "Impaired multisensory processing in schizophrenia: deficits in the visual enhancement of speech comprehension under noisy environmental conditions". *Schizophrenia research* **97** (1-3): 173–183. doi: 10.1016/j.schres.2007.08.008 (http://dx.doi.org/10.1016/j.schres.2007.08.008). ISSN 0920-9964 (http://worldcat.org/issn/0920-9964). PMID 17928202 (http://www.ncbi.nlm.nih.gov/pubmed/17928202).

[2] Leavitt, Vm; Molholm, S; Ritter, W; Shpaner, M; Foxe, Jj (Sep 2007). " Auditory processing in schizophrenia during the middle latency period (10-50 ms): high-density electrical mapping and source analysis reveal subcortical antecedents to early cortical deficits (http://www.pubmedcentral.nih.gov/articlerender.fcgi?tool=pmcentrez&artid=1963354)". *Journal of psychiatry & neuroscience : JPN* **32** (5): 339–53. ISSN 1180-4882 (http://worldcat.org/issn/1180-4882). PMID 17823650 (http://www.ncbi.nlm.nih.gov/pubmed/17823650).

[3] Rabinowicz, Ef; Silipo, G; Goldman, R; Javitt, Dc (Dec 2000). " Auditory sensory dysfunction in schizophrenia: imprecision or distractibility? (http://archpsyc.ama-assn.org/cgi/pmidlookup?view=long&pmid=11115328)" (Free full text). *Archives of general psychiatry* **57** (12): 1149–55. ISSN 0003-990X (http://worldcat.org/issn/0003-990X). PMID 11115328 (http://www.ncbi.nlm.nih.gov/pubmed/11115328). .

[4] Kratz, V. (Jun 2009). "Sensory integration intervention: historical concepts, treatment strategies and clinical experiences in three patients with succinic semialdehyde dehydrogenase (SSADH) deficiency". *Journal of inherited metabolic disease* **32** (3): 353–360. doi: 10.1007/s10545-009-1149-1 (http://dx.doi.org/10.1007/s10545-009-1149-1). ISSN 0141-8955 (http://worldcat.org/issn/0141-8955). PMID 19381864 (http://www.ncbi.nlm.nih.gov/pubmed/19381864).

[5] Tian, Yh; Cheng, H (Oct 2008). "Sensory integration function in children with primary nocturnal enuresis". *Zhongguo dang dai er ke za zhi = Chinese journal of contemporary pediatrics* **10** (5): 611–3. ISSN 1008-8830 (http://worldcat.org/issn/1008-8830). PMID 18947482 (http://www.ncbi.nlm.nih.gov/pubmed/18947482).

[6] *Schneider, L.; Moore, F.; Gajewski, L; Larson, A.; Roberts, D.; Converse, K.; Dejesus, T. (Jan 2008). "Sensory Processing Disorder in a Primate Model: Evidence from a Longitudinal Study of Prenatal Alcohol and Prenatal Stress Effects". *Child Development* **79** (1): 100. doi: 10.1111/j.1467-8624.2007.01113.x (http://dx.doi.org/10.1111/j.1467-8624.2007.01113.x). ISSN 0009-3920 (http://worldcat.org/issn/0009-3920). PMID 18269511 (http://www.ncbi.nlm.nih.gov/pubmed/18269511).

[7] Lane, E.; Young, L.; Baker, E.; Angley, T. (Jul 2009). "Sensory Processing Subtypes in Autism: Association with Adaptive Behavior". *Journal of Autism and Developmental Disorders.* doi: 10.1007/s10803-009-0840-2 (http://dx.doi.org/10.1007/s10803-009-0840-2). ISSN 0162-3257 (http://worldcat.org/issn/0162-3257). PMID 19644746 (http://www.ncbi.nlm.nih.gov/pubmed/19644746).

[8] Tomchek, Sd; Dunn, W (Mar 2007). "Sensory processing in children with and without autism: a comparative study using the short sensory profile". *The American journal of occupational therapy. : official publication of the American Occupational Therapy Association* **61** (2): 190–200. ISSN 0272-9490 (http://worldcat.org/issn/0272-9490). PMID 17436841 (http://www.ncbi.nlm.nih.gov/pubmed/17436841).

[9] Kern, K.; Trivedi, H.; Grannemann, D.; Garver, R.; Johnson, G.; Andrews, A.; Savla, S.; Mehta, A. *et al.* (Mar 2007). "Sensory correlations in autism". *Autism* **11** (2): 123. doi: 10.1177/1362361307075702 (http://dx.doi.org/10.1177/1362361307075702). ISSN 1362-3613 (http://worldcat.org/issn/1362-3613). PMID 17353213 (http://www.ncbi.nlm.nih.gov/pubmed/17353213).

[10] Slobounov, S.; Tutwiler, R.; Sebastianelli, W.; Slobounov, E. (Jul 2006). "Alteration of Postural Responses to Visual Field Motion in Mild Traumatic Brain Injury". *Neurosurgery* **59** (1): 134. doi: 10.1227/01.NEU.0000219197.33182.3F (http://dx.doi.org/10.1227/01.NEU. 0000219197.33182.3F). ISSN 0148-396X (http://worldcat.org/issn/0148-396X). PMID 16823309 (http://www.ncbi.nlm.nih.gov/ pubmed/16823309).

[11] Bharadwaj, Sv; Daniel, Ll; Matzke, Pl (Mar 2009). "Sensory-processing disorder in children with cochlear implants". *The American journal of occupational therapy. : official publication of the American Occupational Therapy Association* **63** (2): 208–13. ISSN 0272-9490 (http:// worldcat.org/issn/0272-9490). PMID 19432059 (http://www.ncbi.nlm.nih.gov/pubmed/19432059).

[12] Heilbroner PL (2005). " Why "sensory integration disorder" is a dubious diagnosis (http://quackwatch.org/01QuackeryRelatedTopics/sid. html)". *QuackWatch.* . Retrieved 2008-06-02.

[13] Newman B (2000). " On inventing your own disorder (http://csicop.com/si/2000-11/)". *Skeptical Inquirer* (http://csicop.com/si/) **24** (6): 56–57. .

Sources

PubMed

Sensory integration dysfunction

- Kaczorowski, A.; Barrantes-Vidal, N.; Kwapil, R. (Aug 2009). "Neurological soft signs in psychometrically identified schizotypy". *Schizophrenia research.* doi: 10.1016/j.schres.2009.06.018 (http://dx.doi.org/10.1016/ j.schres.2009.06.018). ISSN 0920-9964 (http://worldcat.org/issn/0920-9964). PMID 19651490 (http:// www.ncbi.nlm.nih.gov/pubmed/19651490).

- Allison, L.; Gabriel, H.; Schlange, D.; Fredrickson, S. (Dec 2007). "An optometric approach to patients with sensory integration dysfunction". *Optometry (St. Louis, Mo.)* **78** (12): 644–651. doi: 10.1016/j.optm.2007.05.012 (http://dx.doi.org/10.1016/j.optm.2007.05.012). ISSN 1529-1839 (http://worldcat.org/issn/1529-1839). PMID 18054134 (http://www.ncbi.nlm.nih.gov/pubmed/18054134).

- Mailloux, Z; May-Benson, Ta; Summers, Ca; Miller, Lj; Brett-Green, B; Burke, Jp; Cohn, Es; Koomar, Ja; Parham, Ld; Roley, Ss; Schaaf, Rc; Schoen, Sa (Mar 2007). "Goal attainment scaling as a measure of meaningful outcomes for children with sensory integration disorders". *The American journal of occupational therapy. : official publication of the American Occupational Therapy Association* **61** (2): 254–9. ISSN 0272-9490 (http:// worldcat.org/issn/0272-9490). PMID 17436848 (http://www.ncbi.nlm.nih.gov/pubmed/17436848).

- Magalhães, C.; Missiuna, C.; Wong, S. (Nov 2006). "Terminology used in research reports of developmental coordination disorder". *Developmental Medicine & Child Neurology* **48** (11): 937. doi: 10.1017/S0012162206002040 (http://dx.doi.org/10.1017/S0012162206002040). ISSN 0012-1622 (http:// worldcat.org/issn/0012-1622). PMID 17044965 (http://www.ncbi.nlm.nih.gov/pubmed/17044965).

- Keefe, S (Jan 2004). "Sensory integration dysfunction. Recognition in primary care settings". *Advance for nurse practitioners* **12** (1): 57–8. ISSN 1096-6293 (http://worldcat.org/issn/1096-6293). PMID 14730839 (http:// www.ncbi.nlm.nih.gov/pubmed/14730839).

- Kemmis, Bl; Dunn, W (Oct 1996). " Collaborative consultation: the efficacy of remedial and compensatory interventions in school contexts (http://www.nlm.nih.gov/medlineplus/learningdisorders.html)" (Free full text). *The American journal of occupational therapy. : official publication of the American Occupational Therapy Association* **50** (9): 709–17. ISSN 0272-9490 (http://worldcat.org/issn/0272-9490). PMID 8886189 (http:// www.ncbi.nlm.nih.gov/pubmed/8886189).

- Horowitz, Lj; Oosterveld, Wj; Adrichem, R (1993). "Effectiveness of sensory integration therapy on smooth pursuits and organization time in children". *Padiatrie und Grenzgebiete* **31** (5): 331–44. ISSN 0030-932X (http://worldcat.org/issn/0030-932X). PMID 8202321 (http://www.ncbi.nlm.nih.gov/pubmed/8202321).
- Stepp-Gilbert, E (1988). "Sensory integration dysfunction". *Issues in comprehensive pediatric nursing* **11** (5-6): 313–8. ISSN 0146-0862 (http://worldcat.org/issn/0146-0862). PMID 2468631 (http://www.ncbi.nlm.nih.gov/pubmed/2468631).

Sensory processing dysfunction

- Bartley, J. (Mar 2009). "Could glial activation be a factor in migraine?". *Medical Hypotheses* **72** (3): 255–257. doi: 10.1016/j.mehy.2008.09.048 (http://dx.doi.org/10.1016/j.mehy.2008.09.048). ISSN 0306-9877 (http://worldcat.org/issn/0306-9877). PMID 19036526 (http://www.ncbi.nlm.nih.gov/pubmed/19036526).
- Philippe, A.; Boddaert, N.; Vaivre-Douret, L.; Robel, L.; Danon-Boileau, L.; Malan, V.; De Blois, C.; Heron, D. et al. (Aug 2008). " Neurobehavioral Profile and Brain Imaging Study of the 22q13.3 Deletion Syndrome in Childhood (http://pediatrics.aappublications.org/cgi/pmidlookup?view=long&pmid=18625665)" (Free full text). *Pediatrics* **122** (2): e376. doi: 10.1542/peds.2007-2584 (http://dx.doi.org/10.1542/peds.2007-2584). ISSN 0031-4005 (http://worldcat.org/issn/0031-4005). PMID 18625665 (http://www.ncbi.nlm.nih.gov/pubmed/18625665).
- Bundy, Ac; Shia, S; Qi, L; Miller, Lj (Mar 2007). "How does sensory processing dysfunction affect play?". *The American journal of occupational therapy. : official publication of the American Occupational Therapy Association* **61** (2): 201–8. ISSN 0272-9490 (http://worldcat.org/issn/0272-9490). PMID 17436842 (http://www.ncbi.nlm.nih.gov/pubmed/17436842).
- Chow, Sm (Jun 2005). "The suitability of the Sensory Profile for diagnosing sensory modulation dysfunctions in Chinese children". *International journal of rehabilitation research. Internationale Zeitschrift fur Rehabilitationsforschung. Revue internationale de recherches de readaptation* **28** (2): 153–8. ISSN 0342-5282 (http://worldcat.org/issn/0342-5282). PMID 15900186 (http://www.ncbi.nlm.nih.gov/pubmed/15900186).
- Royeen, Cr; Mu, K (2003). "Stability of tactile defensiveness across cultures: European and American children's responses to the Touch Inventory for Elementary school aged children". *Occupational therapy international* **10** (3): 165–74. ISSN 0966-7903 (http://worldcat.org/issn/0966-7903). PMID 12900789 (http://www.ncbi.nlm.nih.gov/pubmed/12900789).

Sensory processing disorder

- Byrne, W. (Jun 2009). "Sensory processing disorder: Any of a nurse practitioner's business?". *Journal of the American Academy of Nurse Practitioners* **21** (6): 314–321. doi: 10.1111/j.1745-7599.2009.00417.x (http://dx.doi.org/10.1111/j.1745-7599.2009.00417.x). ISSN 1041-2972 (http://worldcat.org/issn/1041-2972). PMID 19527310 (http://www.ncbi.nlm.nih.gov/pubmed/19527310).
- Cheng, M; Boggett-Carsjens, J (May 2005). " Consider sensory processing disorders in the explosive child: case report and review (http://www.pubmedcentral.nih.gov/articlerender.fcgi?tool=pubmed&pubmedid=19030515)" (Free full text). *The Canadian child and adolescent psychiatry review = La revue canadienne de psychiatrie de l'enfant et de l'adolescent* **14** (2): 44–8. ISSN 1716-9119 (http://worldcat.org/issn/1716-9119). PMID 19030515 (http://www.ncbi.nlm.nih.gov/pubmed/19030515). PMC 2542921 (http://www.pubmedcentral.nih.gov/articlerender.fcgi?tool=pmcentrez&artid=2542921).
- Brett-Green, A.; Miller, J.; Gavin, J.; Davies, L. (Nov 2008). "Multisensory integration in children: A preliminary ERP study". *Brain Research* **1242**: 283. doi: 10.1016/j.brainres.2008.03.090 (http://dx.doi.org/10.1016/j.brainres.2008.03.090). ISSN 0006-8993 (http://worldcat.org/issn/0006-8993). PMID 18495092 (http://www.ncbi.nlm.nih.gov/pubmed/18495092).

Other sources

- Case-Smith, Jane. (2005) *Occupational Therapy for Children*. 5th Edn. Elsevier Mosby: St. Louis, MO. ISBN 032302873X
- Biel, Lindsey and Peske, Nancy. (2005) *Raising A Sensory Smart Child*. Penguin: New York. ISBN 014303488X, website: http://www.sensorysmarts.com
- Heller, Sharon, Ph.D., 2003. "Too Loud, Too Bright, Too Fast, Too Tight: What to do if you are sensory defensive in an overstimulating world.", Quill: New York. ISBN 0-06-019520-7 or 0-06-093292-9 (pbk.) ((Focuses on Adults))
- Schaaf, R.C., and L.J. Miller. 2005. "Occupational therapy using a sensory integrative approach for children with developmental disabilities", *Ment. Retard. Dev. Disabil. Res. Rev.* 11(2):143-148.
- Herbert JD, Sharp IR, Gaudiano BA (2002). " Separating fact from fiction in the etiology and treatment of autism: a scientific review of the evidence (http://www.srmhp.org/0101/autism.html)". *Sci Rev Ment Health Pract* **1** (1): 23–43.

Sluggish cognitive tempo

Sluggish Cognitive Tempo (SCT) is an unformalized descriptive term which is used to better identify what appears to be a homogeneous sub-subgroup within the formal subgroup → ADHD predominantly inattentive (ADHD-I or ADHD-PI) classification in the → Diagnostic and Statistical Manual of Mental Disorders, fourth edition. It has been roughly estimated that the SCT population may make up 30-50% of the ADHD-PI population.

In many ways, those who have an SCT profile have the opposite symptoms of those with classic ADHD: Instead of being hyperactive, extroverted, obtrusive, and risk takers, those with SCT are passive, daydreamy, shy, and HYPO-active in both a mental and physical way. They also don't have the same risk factors and outcomes. Their demeanor is sluggish, as if "in a fog" and logically they also process information more slowly. A key behavioural characteristic of those with SCT symptoms is that they are more likely to appear to be lacking motivation. They lack energy to deal with mundane tasks and will consequently seek things that are mentally stimulating because of their underaroused state. Those with SCT symptoms show a qualitatively different kind of attention deficit that is more typical of a true information input-output problem, such as memory retrieval and active working memory. Conversely, those with the other two subtypes of ADHD are characteristically excessively energetic and have no difficulty processing information.[1]

Diagnosis

Since the symptoms of SCT are not recognized in any standard medical manuals, those who have significant SCT symptoms would likely receive an ADHD/PI diagnosis. Currently the APA will most likely include SCT in the DSM-V, which is scheduled to be released in 2012.[2] Diagnostic criteria will be determined.

Causes

Like ADHD, those with SCT symptoms have a condition that appears to be genetic in nature. Far less is known about this group yet the impairments seem to indicate the prefrontal cortex region of the brain and difficulties with working memory. The 7-repeat allele polymorphism of the DRD4 gene is also linked more strongly to this group than to ADHD/C and ADHD/PHI subgroups.[3]

It is thought that SCT, ADHD-PI, and ADHD are due to variations in the availability of dopamine and norepinephrine, and/or the efficiency of the large chemical structures of the specific receptors and re-uptake receptors. This would explain the efficacy of stimulants such as amphetamines on the treatment of ADHD and SCT.

Treatment

Up to 90% of children with ADHD respond well to methylphenidate (Ritalin) at medium-to-high doses[4] , however, a sizable percentage of children with ADHD-PI do not gain much benefit from Ritalin, and when they do benefit, it is at a much lower dose. Tests in lab rats have demonstrated that low doses of Ritalin can increase norepinephrine levels.

Those with ADHD-PI often respond well to amphetamines, such as the prescription medication Adderall. While methylphenidate and amphetamines have many similar effects on patients (both inhibit reuptake of the neurotransmitters dopamine and norepinephrine, for example), amphetamines also promote release of those neurotransmitters. This positive effect appears to support the hypothesis that SCT is related to neurotransmitter deficiencies.

Prognosis

ADHD is a developmental disorder, meaning that certain traits will be delayed in the ADHD individual. These traits can and usually will develop in people with ADHD, but just at a much slower rate than the average person. With ADHD, it has been estimated that this lag could be as high as thirty to forty percent in the development of certain skill sets, such as selective attention. Symptoms of ADHD are often seen by the time a child enters preschool. Those with SCT symptoms typically show a later onset of symptoms in comparison to ADHD. They have greater difficulty with academic tasks and far fewer social difficulties when compared to those with combo and hyperactive ADHD.

Selective attention difficulties of those with SCT manifests itself academically, in that they are prone to making more mistakes while working. Those with classic ADHD do not have this difficulty. Those with SCT have difficulty with verbal retrieval from long term memory, but may have greater visual spatial capabilities. They have deficits in working memory which has been described as the ability to keep multiple things in mind for manipulation, while simultaneously keeping this information free from internal distraction. Consequently, mental skills such as calculation, reading, and abstract reasoning are often more challenging for those with SCT. They also have a more disorganized thought process, a greater degree of sloppiness, and lose things more easily. They tend to have a greater degree of comorbid learning disabilities. Instead of having greater difficulty selecting and filtering sensory input, as is in the case of SCT, people with other types of ADHD have problems with inhibition.

Studies indicate that comorbid psychiatric problems are more often of the internalizing variety with SCT, such as anxiety, depression, and social withdrawal. Their typical shy nature and slow response time has often been misinterpreted as aloofness or disinterest by others. In social group interactions, those with SCT may be ignored. Those with the other types of ADHD are more likely to be rejected in social situations, because of more intrusive or aggressive behavior. Those with classic ADHD also show externalizing problems such as substance abuse, oppositional-defiant disorder, and, to a lesser degree, conduct disorder.[1] [5]

Prevention

There is no known way to prevent ADHD/PI. Some studies indicate an association between mothers who smoke during pregnancy and a higher rate of ADHD in their children. Avoiding smoking, alcohol, and drugs during pregnancy may help reduce the risk of developing ADHD or similar behaviour in offspring.

History of the term SCT and its relationship to the DSM

Sluggishness, drowsiness, and daydreaming were the characteristics listed in the DSM-III (in use from 1980-1987) that were to also be present in the diagnosis of Attention Deficit Disorder (ADD) without Hyperactivity. In a study looking at these symptoms (Lahey et al., 1988) the authors stated, "these symptoms were statistically extracted as a distinct factor", coined, Sluggish Cognitive Tempo. The Sluggish Tempo factor was found to correlate significantly to the Inattention factor, but only when Hyperactivity-Impulsivity symptoms were absent.

Sluggish Cognitive Tempo symptoms were removed from the Inattention symptom list in 1988 because of poor negative predictive power for the inattentive subgroup, and because DSM contributors and editors wanted the inattentive symptoms to be identical for all ADHD subgroups. The presence of the SCT symptoms tended to predict inattention, but the absence of these symptoms did not predict the absence of inattention.[6] This analysis did not take into account the possibility that the SCT symptoms could help predict a distinct grouping within the ADHD/PI subgroup and that the ADHD/PI subgrouping could be heterogeneous in nature.[7]

In the DSM-IV, with its new classification of symptoms for predominately inattentive ADHD, 50 to 70% of those with a ADHD-PI diagnosis have subclinical levels of hyperactivity-impulsiveness symptoms. People with ADHD combined type (ADHD-C) and predominantly hyperactive–impulsive type (ADHD-PHI) may outgrow some, or most of their hyperactive symptoms during or after childhood, while inattentive symptoms typically remain into adulthood. In contrast, those with SCT have had only inattentive features from a young age with little to no history of hyperactivity-impulsiveness. Dr. Russell Barkley has proposed that the DSM-IV designation of ADHD-PI be used only for those displaying purely inattentive symptoms and that those who have had a history of *any* hyperactivity be designated as ADHD combined subtype. Currently, one can have a few hyperactive symptoms and still receive a diagnosis ADHD-PI. Others believe that SCT should be classified as a new separate disorder when the DSM is next updated.[3]

Relationship to dysexecutive syndrome

The Executive system of the human brain coordinates actions and strategies for everyday tasks. Dysexecutive syndrome is defined as "cluster of impairments generally associated with damage to the frontal lobes of the brain" which includes "difficulties with high-level tasks such as planning, organising, initiating, monitoring and adapting behaviour."[8]

Adele Diamond has recently postulated that the core cognitive deficit of those with ADHD-PI (ADD), is working memory, or, as she coined in her recent paper on the subject, "childhood-onset dysexecutive syndrome". She states:

- "Instructional methods that place heavy demands on working memory will disproportionately disadvantage individuals with ADD".
- "language problems often co-occur with ADD, and it is suggested that part of the reason might be that linguistic tasks, especially verbal ones, tax working memory so heavily. Spatial and artistic skills, however, are often preserved or superior in individuals with ADD."
- "The working memory deficit in many children with ADD is accompanied by markedly slowed reaction times, a characteristic that covaries with poorer working memory in general".
- "Individuals with ADD have difficulty maintaining a sufficiently high level of motivation to complete a task...They go looking for something else to do or think about because they are bored...to remedy a general lower arousal level.."[3]

See also

- → Attention-deficit hyperactivity disorder
- → ADHD predominantly inattentive
- Dysthymia
- Hypothyroidism

External links

- ADHD: Nature, Course, Outcomes, and Comorbidity by Russell A. Barkley, Ph.D. [9]
- Attention-deficit disorder (attention-deficit/hyperactivity disorder without hyperactivity): A neurobiologically and behaviorally distinct disorder from attention-deficit/hyperactivity disorder (with hyperactivity) by ADELE DIAMOND [10]
- Dr. Russell Barkley on ADHD. [11] (SCT is mentioned in the second section of the lecture notes entitled: "is Inattentive ADHD really another disorder")
- An interview with Richard Milich entitled, "Lost in the shuffle - the inattentive child without hyperactivity" [12]
- ADHD Combined and ADHD Predominantly Inattentive Type are Distinct and unrelated disorders by Milich et al. [13]

References

[1] Dr. Russell Barkley: AD/HD Theory, Diagnosis, & Treatment Summary (http://www.schwablearning.org/articles.aspx?r=54)

[2] http://www.youtube.com/watch?v=q3d1SwUXMc0&e

[3] Diamond, Adele Attention-deficit disorder (attention-deficit/hyperactivity disorder without hyperactivity): A neurobiologically and behaviorally distinct disorder from attention-deficit/hyperactivity disorder (with hyperactivity) (http://www.pubmedcentral.nih.gov/articlerender.fcgi?artid=1474811) *Development and Psychopathology* 17: 807-825 Cambridge University Press (2005)

[4] Diamond, Adele, "Attention-deficit disorder (attention-deficit/hyperactivity disorder without hyperactivity): A neurobiologically and behaviorally distinct disorder from attention-deficit/hyperactivity disorder (with hyperactivity)" (http://www.pubmedcentral.nih.gov/articlerender.fcgi?artid=1474811), (2006)

[5] Barkley, Russell Attention-Deficit/Hyperactivity Disorder: Nature, Course, Outcomes, and Comorbidity (http://www.continuingedcourses.net/active/courses/course003.php)

[6] Blackwell Synergy - Clin Psychol Sci & Pract, Volume 8 Issue 4 Page 463-488, December 2001 (Article Abstract) (http://www.blackwell-synergy.com/doi/abs/10.1093/clipsy.8.4.463)

[7] Symptom properties as a function of ADHD type: an ...[J Abnorm Child Psychol. 2001] - PubMed Result (http://www.ncbi.nlm.nih.gov/entrez/query.fcgi?cmd=Retrieve&db=PubMed&list_uids=11411783&dopt=Abstract)

[8] http://www.dwp.gov.uk/advisers/joped/vol5/no2_sum_03_test_review_2.pdf

[9] http://www.continuingedcourses.net/active/courses/course003.php

[10] http://www.pubmedcentral.nih.gov/articlerender.fcgi?artid=1474811

[11] http://www.schwablearning.org/articles.asp?r=54

[12] http://www.chadd.org/AM/Template.cfm?Section=Attention_Magazine&Template=/CM/ContentDisplay.cfm&ContentID=3347.

[13] http://www.blackwell-synergy.com/doi/abs/10.1093/clipsy.8.4.463

Wilson's syndrome

Wilson's (temperature) syndrome, also called **Wilson's thyroid syndrome** or WTS, is an alternative medical diagnosis consisting of various common and non-specific symptoms which are attributed to the thyroid, despite normal thyroid function tests. E. Denis Wilson, a physician who named the syndrome after himself, advocates treating these symptoms with a special preparation of triiodothyronine.

Wilson's syndrome is not recognized as a medical condition by mainstream medicine. The American Thyroid Association (ATA) describes Wilson's syndrome as at odds with established knowledge of thyroid function. The ATA reported a lack of supporting scientific evidence as well as aspects of Wilson's claims which were inconsistent with "well-known and widely-accepted facts" concerning the functions of the thyroid, and raised concern that the proposed treatments were potentially harmful.[1]

Origins, claims, and disciplinary action

Wilson's syndrome was coined by E. Denis Wilson, M.D., of Longwood, Florida in 1990. Wilson said that the syndrome's manifestations included symptoms typical of low thyroid function such as fatigue, headaches, PMS, hair loss, irritability, fluid retention, depression, decreased memory, low sex drive, unhealthy nails, easy weight gain, and about 60 other symptoms. Wilson says that WTS can manifest itself as "virtually every symptom known to man". He also says that it is "the most common of all chronic ailments and probably takes a greater toll on society than any other medical condition".[2]

Wilson says that low thyroid symptoms and low temperatures in the presence of normal thyroid function tests are not due to hypothyroidism, and might be reversed with a few months of treatment. To distinguish this condition from hypothyroidism, he named it Wilson's (temperature) syndrome. He states that it is "especially brought on by stress" and can persist after the stress has passed. He says that the main diagnostic sign is a body temperature that averages below 98.6 °F (37.0 °C) (oral), and that the diagnosis is confirmed if the patient responds to treatment with a "special thyroid hormone treatment". He says that certain herbs can also help support normal body temperatures. According to Wilson,[3] persons whose body temperature is routinely below 98.2 °F (36.8 °C) should be tested for hypothyroidism using the thyroid stimulating hormone (TSH) test. However, if a person's body temperature is low and the test is normal, Wilson argues that the person may have Wilson's Temperature Syndrome.

In 1988 a 50-year-old woman died of an arrhythmia and heart attack while taking excessive amounts of thyroid hormone prescribed by Wilson, around that time she confessed to not taking the medicine as regularly as prescribed. [4] Four years later, in 1992, the Florida Board of Medicine took disciplinary action against Wilson,[5] The Board of Medicine and Wilson settled the disciplinary action by entering into a "consent agreement" specifying that in order to resume practice after a 6 month suspension Dr. Wilson would need to attend 100 hours of continuing medical education, submit to psychological testing, pay a $10,000 fine, and not prescribe any thyroid medicine to anyone unless and until the Board of Medicine determines that the medical community has accepted "Wilson's Syndrome" and Wilson's methods and modalities of treatment.[4] [6]

Evaluations

One uncontrolled study of 11 patients reported positive results with Wilson's therapy.[7] It is also popular in complementary and alternative medicine practices, and is being taught in naturopathic medical schools.[8]

The American Thyroid Association (ATA), a professional association dedicated to promoting thyroid health, disavows Wilson's Syndrome. The ATA stated in 2005 that a "thorough review of the biomedical literature has found no scientific evidence supporting the existence of 'Wilson's Syndrome'."[1]

References

[1] " ATA Statement on "Wilson's Syndrome" (http://www.thyroid.org/professionals/publications/statements/99_11_16_wilsons.html)". American Thyroid Association. .

[2] Wilson, E. Denis (1992). *Wilson's Temperature Syndrome - A Reversible Low Temperature Problem*. Cornerstone Publishing. ISBN 09708510-1-4.

[3] Wilson's Temperature Syndrome - Hypothyroidism - Hypothyroid - Thyroid disease (http://www.wilsonssyndrome.com/)

[4] State of Florida, Department of Health; Date: 02-12-1992; Final Order Number: DPR9200039ME

[5] " License Verification: E. Denis Wilson (http://ww2.doh.state.fl.us/irm00PRAES/PRASINDI.asp?LicId=40535&ProfNBR=1501)". Florida Department of Health. . Retrieved April 2, 2009.

[6] Berdanier, Carol, ed (2002). *Handbook of Nutrition and Food* (http://books.google.com/books?id=ysrzdCPc4dAC). CRC Press. p. 1498. ISBN 9780849327056. . Retrieved April 2, 2009.

[7] Friedman M, Miranda-Massari JR, Gonzalez MJ (2006). "Supraphysiological cyclic dosing of sustained release T3 in order to reset low basal body temperature.". *P R Health Sci J.* **25** (1): 23–9. PMID 16883675 (http://www.ncbi.nlm.nih.gov/pubmed/16883675).

[8] Friedman, Michael (2005). *Fundamentals of Naturopathic Medicine*. Canadian College of Naturopathic Medicine Press. ISBN 1-897025-02-5.

Article Sources and Contributors

ADHD predominantly inattentive *Source*: http://en.wikipedia.org/w/index.php?title=ADHD_predominantly_inattentive *Contributors*: A3RO, Adhdmom, Alanraywiki, Alec.brady, Alexfusco5, Antiedman, Beefyt, Beetstra, Bobo192, COMPFUNK2, Calvin 1998, CardinalDan, Ccacsmss, Chacehensley, Clayoquot, Clh288, Cobi, Corvus cornix, Cst17, D'Agosta, DCDuring, Da monster under your bed, DashaKat, Dawn Bard, Decoy, Delldot, Djma12, Doghead777, GPattle, Gaz2inf, Georgette2, Greenmanwitch, JiFish, Jonpaulusa, Jonverve, Keilana, Lova Falk, Mattisse, McSly, Megaman en m, Mmortal03, Necie B, Ned Scott, Norum370, ONEder Boy, Ofus, Ojcookies, Peterseb, QWENTYU, RedAlgorithm, Renovation, Richi, S1lenze, Scuro, Sohale, Sonjaaa, Sriram sh, SuperHamster, TMC1982, Tanthalas39, Tdowling, Terrym2442, Tiddly Tom, Tinton5, Tom, Utoks, Versageek, 88 anonymous edits

Attention-deficit hyperactivity disorder *Source*: http://en.wikipedia.org/w/index.php?title=Attention-deficit_hyperactivity_disorder *Contributors*: *Kat*, 07tghard, 2005, 4shockblast, A little insignificant, A13542, A314268, A8UDI, AI, AThing, AVand, AZDub, Aaabbbttx, Aaron Brenneman, Abce2, Abd, Accurizer, Acebulf, Aces lead, Acidskater, Action potential, Acuozzo, Adam Conover, Adam318, Adashiel, Add-advocate, Addontheweb, Adrian0101, Afaprof01, Agilemongoose, Aitias, Ajaxkroon, Alan J Shea, Alan Liefting, Alansohn, Alasdair, Ale jrb, Alex6015, Alexfusco5, Alexnye, Alexoppenheim, Alfie66, Alfredo Arredondo, Allen3, Allysizzle, Althealth, Alvis Jean, Amanojyaku, Amcbride, Ameliorate!, Amillar, Amy tremaine, AmyNelson, Ancadi, Andre Engels, Andrewgio, Andrewudstraw, Andyh2, Angelic Wraith, AngieDixon, Aniruhama, Annmarena, Anonymaus, Antaeus Feldspar, Apoc2400, Apokrif, Aport2, Appraiser, Aranel, Arcadian, Ardonik, Armarshall, Aroboy93, Arrow Fife, Arthur Rubin, ArthurDenture, Aryeeka, Asgrim, Astanhope, Aston Villa, Astronaut, Athanasius1, Atshields0, Aulis Eskola, Awien, Ayotte, AzaToth, Azzors, BD2412, Back ache, Barbara Shack, Barfooz, Barkleyr, Barneca, Barrylb, Bastique, Bbatsell, Bear475, Beetstra, Bellyoffire, Bemoeial, Ben Ben, Bencherlite, Berkeley99, Bigwhite16, Bill Hewitt, BillWestman, Billyg, Binary TSO, Biscuittin, Bishonen, Bk0, Blackmamba13, Blade21cn, Blashyrk, Blingbling1000, Blinksublime, Bliskner, Blshaw, Bobblewik, Bobianite, Bobula666, Bondi007, Bongwarrior, Boothy443, Boradis, Bradleyfrank, Brettgo1, Brian0918, Brian132, BrianGCrawfordMA, BrianKnez, Brighterorange, Brsma, Bruce89, Bstedman, Bubba73, Bumhoolery, C6541, CDN99, CHADD-NRC, CMacMillan, CWii, Cab88, Cahum, Caltas, Can't sleep, clown will eat me, Canadian-Bacon, CanadianLinuxUser, Canderson7, CanisRufus, Canterbury Tail, Capricorn42, CaptainLexicon, CarTick, CardinalDan, Carlossuarez46, Casliber, CesarB, Cgingold, ChadThomson, Chamal N, Channel4, Chapintb, Charles.hamilton95, Charlesriver, Chase Biblow, Chewy200890, Chickyfuzz14, Chipmonkandco, Chowbok, Chris Capoccia, Chris is me, Christopher Mann McKay, Chub, Chwats, Cityzen451, Clam0p, Clarknova, Claycountyinlaw, Clh288, CliffC, Clintonleefitz, Clockback, CloudSurfer, Cmdrjameson, Cminard, Coach4learn, Coffeetree, Coffeezombie, Colin, Colonies Chris, Cometpants, Computerjoe, Contentmaven, Conti, Coolhandscot, Corinned, Corinnedavies, Cpbaylis, Cprompt, Creidieki, Cretog8, Cue the Strings, Curious1i, CurtisJohnson, Cwager, Cyhatch, Cynthiahammer, Cypher056E, D, D'Agosta, DCDuring, DEaF TO LiGhT, DGG, DMG413, DRyan, DVD R W, Da monster under your bed, DabMachine, Damnreds, Daniel123297, DanielCD, Dannykean, Dareu2move, Dark3352, DarkFalls, Dash, DashaKat, Database, Dave-ros, DavidFarmbrough, Dawn Bard, Dchico6, Dddstone, Ddhix 2002, DearPrudence, Deathawk, Debresser, Deli nk, Delma1, Denali134, Dendritelady, Dep. Garcia, DerHexer, Derex, Destynova, Dhodges, Diberri, Diderot, Dima373, DirkOliverTheis, Discooo, Discospinster, Dissembly, Djcraze, Dkpoto, Dlohcierekim, Doady, DoctorW, Dogface, Dolfrog, Dolive21, DomQ, Doniago, Dorfy0001, Douglas Bradford Oliver, Dr Taba, Dragonkin877, Dragonnas, Drew R. Smith, Driven Jen, Drsrshahmd, Drumex, Drumnbassno3, Dspradau, Dtanton, DuganPorter, Duncan.france, Durin, E0steven, E946, ERobson, ESkog, Ebonyg, Edbeckham, Edgar181, Edison, Editor182, Edward, Edward Bower, Ehheh, ElBenevolente, ElJayDee, ElKevbo, ElectricTrivia, Ellenmc, Emilyxlovesxyou, Enigmaman, Enohpesrep, Enric Naval, Enviroboy, Epbr123, Ericurs, Eridanis, Erik9, Ermo200, Espoo, Esprit Salut, Eubulides, Evil genius, Excirial, Explicit, Extremecircuitz, Extremeddrfreak, Ezratrumpet, Ezzibbzxx, F w element, Fadhd2, Falcon8765, Faradayplank, Feezo, Fences and windows, Fieldday-sunday, Fipher, Flewis, Flowanda, Fobrox97, Food views, ForesticPig, FrankTobia, Frankenpuppy, Franklinjefferson, Freerick, Fremte, Furrykef, Fuzzform, GHULAMSADIQUE, GT, Gaddyy2, Gaius Cornelius, Gakrivas, Galaxiaad, Galizia, Garrondo, Gary King, Garybradski, GavinTing, Gaz2inf, Gene Nygaard, Geoffrey Gibson, Gidonb, Ginkgo100, Gjl, GoPlayerJuggler, Gondwanabanana, Googie man, Gosolowe, GouFei, Gracenotes, GraemeL, Graham87, Grandpabailey, Greenbenuk, Greenmanwitch, Gregnz, Grika, Gsandi, Guacmol, Guatemala69, Guitarpicks, Guitarted345, Gurch, Gwernol, Gzkn, Gzuckier, HOUZI, Hadal, Hagaland, Halmstad, HamburgerRadio, Hannabee, Haseo9999, Havermayer, Headwes, Hede2000, Hello32020, Henry W. Schmitt, HeteroZellous, HistoricalPisces, Histrion, Hlangeveld, Hlarson, Hmwith, HoodedMan, Horatio wells, Hordaland, Horst.Burkhardt, House of Usher, Husond, Hut 6.5, Hyacinth, Hydrogen Iodide, Hyperion35, Hypnoses, II MusLiM HyBRiD II, IIIIIIIIIP-OIIIIIIIII, Iamsmitty, IanOsgood, IanWills, Ianblair23, Ianupright, Iapetus, Ice Ardor, Icek, Icewedge, Ichbinkerl, Ida Shaw, Ignignot, Ihaveaids, Ilikeclubsoda, IloveMT, Ilovemassachusetts84, ImperfectlyInformed, In Defense of the Artist, Insaneinside, Insanity Incarnate, Invincible Ninja, Irbisgreif, Iridescent, Irishguy, Isogolem, Itappedthat, Ixfd64, J Di, J.delanoy, JHunterJ, JaGa, Jacoplane, Jakarr, Jamason123, James pic, James086, JamesTeterenko, Jamesandchristian, Jamesters, Janeb, Jasonmark, Jatos, Jaxl, Jayden54, Jcemcare, Jcrock, Jcsquardo, Jdboone21, Jedibob5, Jeff Silvers, Jellonuts, Jennavecia, JeremyA, JeroenMassar, Jevinsweval, Jewman1432, Jeyradan, Jfdwolff, JiFish, Jkhamlin, Jkorbes, Jla 2000, Jmh649, Jmw0000, Jocomama, JoeHine, Joeclark, Jogloran, Johann Gambolputty, John254, JohnsonRon, Jollygood, Jonathan Drain, Jonund, Jonverve, Jose Ramos, Josh1203, Joshrival, Jossi, Jowmackenzie, Jpgordon, Jpstead, JulesH, Julesd, Jumbuck, Junglecat, KTC, KTLane, Kafziel, Kakofonous, Kalliope, Kasreyn, Kata Alreshim, KathrynLybarger, KatiaRoma, Katieb44, Kbdank71, Kbh3rd, Kdbuffalo, Keegan, Keilana, Kelbel119, Kendrick7, Keno, Khoikhoi, Khono, Killath303, Killroyomega, Kingturtle, Kisama, KittyLam, Kmontgo, Knightkid123, Koavf, Konstable, KoshVorlon, Koweja, Krikkit4, Kslays, Kubigula, KurtRaschke, Kuru, Kyle1278, Kyried, LTSally, Lancier, Landcamera900, Landindonner, Lapytopy, Largo the l33t ma5t3r, Larsklintwallmalmqvist, LastChance, Latka, Laudaka, Lawikitejana, Lcgarcia, Learnthesigns, LeaveSleaves, Legit-Anti-Psychiatry101, Letterneversent, Leuko, Lifeartist, Liftarn, Lightdarkness, Lightmouse, Limegreen, Limideen, Link13090, Linkspamremover, Literaturegeek, LittleDan, LittleMissStrange, LittlegreenmanfromMars, Logictheo, Loren.wilton, Lorn, Lova Falk, Luna Santin, Lunakeet, LuvMe13, MER-C, Macapa, Madewokherd, Malinaccier, Man It's So Loud In Here, Mani1, Manuel Pesqué, Marcika, Marcos800, Marek69, Mark in wiki, Markaci, Markkawika, Markus451, MarkusSchulze, Martial Law, Martin48535, Martinog, Martinq22, Marudubshinki, MastCell, MattKingston, Matthew111688, Matthewedgar, Mattwiley, Matty005, Mav, Mavadnais, Max.coke, Mb1000, Mbhutten, Mboverload, McLeod1, McSly, Mcmd, Mdukas, Meagannnn, Meco, Meg1064, Mel Etitis, MeltBanana, Mentifisto, Mentxx2, Metaquasi, Miakoda30, Michael Hardy, MichaelMaggs, Michele123, Michelvoss, MickWest, Midgetdan, Mike2vil, Minesweeper, Missdipsy, Mistress Selina Kyle, MitchDuncan, Mj9918, Mnp, Modster, Modulatum, Mohjlir, Mojomama, Mothmolevna, Mpoult25, Mpulier, Mr Bungle, Mr Stephen, MrHat1065, MrOllie, MrTroy, Mrdectol, Mrwimby, Msteelman1, Mtribe, Mulgul, Multixfer, My password is DROLE, Nakon, Nandesuka, Natgoo, Nationofjoe, Naturalpsychology, NatusRoma, NawlinWiki, Nborders1972, Ned Scott, NellieBly, Neothemagic, Nephron, Nesbit, Neurodivergent, NewEnglandYankee, Nicenjuicy, Nickdc, Nickj, Nightscream, Nihil novi, Nja247, No-Bullet, Noah Salzman, Noidontliekmudkipz, Nonpareility, Normane, Nosleep, NothingMuch, Nowa, NuclearWarfare, NuclearWinner, Nunh-huh, ONEder Boy, Oda Mari, Ofus, Ohnoitsjamie, Ojcookies, Olathe, Oldag07, Olivier, Ombudsman, Omega025, Omicronpersei8, OmriSegal, Oneiros, Oneismany, Onorem, OrcinusOrca7, Orion11M87, Orlady, Oswaldojh, OtterSmith, Owl 2, Oxymoron83, Oyyou, P33M, PM Poon, PRMerkley, PaperTruths, Parent1, Pathless, Patm7, Paul Erik, Paulattardb, Paulr, Pavel Vozenilek, Peak, Peruvianllama, PeteThePill, Peter G Werner, Peter-ZA, Petesmiles, Petral-1, Pharaoh of the Wizards, Philip Trueman, PhilipR, Phoik, Pierre-Alain Gouanvic, PierreAbbat, PiggyKrap, Pinklitigation, Piotrus, Pipedreambomb, Pithecanthropus, Pixel ;-), Pizza1512, Pollinosisss, Possum, Powellquiring, PranksterTurtle, Prashanthns, Prislobo, Promethean, Promonk3, Proofer47, Prowikipedians, Psalmuel, PuzzletChung, Pyrospirit, QRX, Qrc2006, Quadell, Quanathon, Quantum bird, Quibbles, Quji, Qviri, RFerreira, RMFan1, RTCearly, Rahuagra502, RainR, Rakel, o, Rashad9607, Rasmus Faber, Raven in Orbit, Red Act, RedAlgorithm, RedHillian, Reisio, Retired username, RexNL, Rhopkins8, Rich Farmbrough, RichardF, Richi, Richwales, Rjwilmsi, Rmosler2100, Rmrfstar, Rob Russell, Robdurbar, Roberta F., Romanpoet, Ronhjones, Ronz, Rosmoran, Rowlandd, RoyBoy, Rror, Runa27, Rursus, Russell E, Rustong141, Ryanaxp, Ryulong, S-k-k, SJaneM, SRK2000, Sadavis, Sally wonder, Samdeskin, Samillia, Sampi, SandyGeorgia, Sango123, Sannse, Sapiens23, Sapphy15, Sarahgeorge, SarekOfVulcan, Sarkar112, SaschaTeske, Sassi72, Satori Son, Scarpy, Sceptre, ScienceApologist, Scorchsaber, Scottydude, Scuro, Sdorrance, Sean Whitton, SeanMack, Seanetal, Sebastian Cartwright, Sebastian406, Seddes, SentoDude, Sethery, Sfahey, ShadowHntr, Shanes, Sheselev, ShiraShira, Shoeofdeath, Shorty7222, Shulae, Sifaka, SineWave, Sir Nicholas de Mimsy-Porpington, Sirusblack16, Sjb0926, Sjw, Skapur, Skater6761, Slashme, Smalljim, Snailgoop, Snakepoop, Snowfairy 33, Soakologist, SophisticatedPrimate, Sopranosmob781, SoulRiser, Spazzman06, Speace, Spencer052002, SpencerThiel, Srice13, Ss06470, Sss180b, Starwarsblows1, StaticGull, Stealthphreak, Steffen Schneider, Stephenb, SteveCrook, SteveSims, Stevenfruitsmaak, Sugarfish, SummerPhD, Summersky77, Supernathan, Surfeited, SweetMelissaGT, Sweetjessica, Swikid, Synthesize, Sysy, TVedder, Ta bu shi da yu, Tabletop, Tagishsimon, Tallen42, Tarquin, Taw, Tdowling, TehBrandon, TennysonXII, Terrym2442, TexasAndroid, The Cat and the Owl, The Duke of Waltham, The Letter J, The Thing That Should Not Be, The9898, Thedjatclubrock, Thehelpfulone, Thelightpoursoutofme, Thingg, ThreeDee912, Tiddly Tom, Tide rolls, Tightjeans101, TimVickers, Timwi, Tiresais, Tkdman99, Tlim7882, Tlusťa, Todeswalzer, Tom, Tom bagley, Tom harrison, Tom.k, Tomchiukc, Touch Of Light, Transity, Tree Biting Conspiracy, Trilobitealive, Tristano Ajmone, Tronno, Trugster, Tseay11, Turkeyphant, TutterMouse, Tweisbach, Typobox, Tznkai, Uncle G, UniAce, UninvitedCompany, Unionhawk, Unknown entity, Unschool, Until It Sleeps, Urod, Usgnus, V In The Know, V10young1, VMHman, Vannin, Vaoverland, Varunkhare, VegKilla, Verbal, Versageek, Vicente ribeiro, Vikingstad, Violetriga, ViriiK, Vishakha, Vishnava, Vizonari, WadeSimMiser, Waggers, Wallendiner66, Walshga, Ward3001, Wavelength, Wayward, Webjunkie, Werldwayd, Wes45, Weyes, Whatamldoing, Whatever404, Whicky1978, Whitebox, Whsc1, WikHead, Wiki alf, Wikibofh, Wikiborg, WikipedianAndrew, WikipedianMarlith, Wikipuddin, Wikiscient, Wikiwikivideo, Wildpinto, William conway bcc, Williamrobinsonb, Wissons, Wknight94, Wmahan, Wolfklinger, Woohookitty, Wouterstomp, Wtmitchell, XTerminator2000, Xadith12, Xasodfuih, Xavexgoem, Xiaden, Xiaphias, Yamamoto Ichiro, Yhc1973, Yuckfoo, Yukichigai, Zanimum, Zaphraud, Zeid Orgorum, Zenex13, Zenohockey, Zigger, Zizonus, Zoicon5, Zzuuzz, Zziggyman, Ævar Arnfjörð Bjarmason, דודי55, 2185 anonymous edits

Diagnostic and Statistical Manual of Mental Disorders *Source*: http://en.wikipedia.org/w/index.php?title=Diagnostic_and_Statistical_Manual_of_Mental_Disorders *Contributors*: 213.253.39.xxx, 66.81.45.xxx, AThing, Abarry, Action potential, Alan Nicoll, Alex.n.darosa, Amorrow, Andre Engels, AnneFrankly, Aranel, Axlq, BRENTKINGBINKY, Barry Jameson, Beefyt, Belovedfreak, Bert56, Blainster, Blharlan, Bluptr, Bmistler, Bobblewik, Bobo192, Bokarius, BoomerAB, Born2x, Bradd, Braincop, Briaboru, Brion VIBBER, Btyner, Bush for mayor, C.P. Arun, Capricorn42, Carl von Blixen, Carnildo, Cdw1952, Chinasaur, Chowbok, ChrisCork, Clane5212, Clemmy, CloudSurfer, Colenso, Conversion script, Cortamears, Cough, Count Caspian, Crackerbelly, Craftyminion, Cremley, CrookedAsterisk, Crum375, Cswrye, Cwirtanen, Cybercobra, Cyrius, DPeterson, Dana boomer, Dancanm, Danielhaggar, Darren J H, Davidp, Delirium, DerHexer, Diberri, Dicklyon, DocWatson42, Doczilla, Donreed, Dpr, Drgarden, Drkencarter, Drugonot, Duagloth, EPM, Eastlaw, Editor2020, Edwy, El C, Eliz81, Emijrp, Epbr123, Eranb, Erikpatt, Eubulides, EverSince, Expo512, Facts707, Fang Aili, Feyre, Figmillenium, Flyer22, Foober, Franzio, Frecklefoot, Fredalottie, Freunlaven47, Fsk, Fvasconcellos, G Rose, Gakrivas, Genesis12, Ghaly, Glane23, Govtagent82, Gurch, Gökhan, Haemo, Hercule, Hherman8, Homebuilding, Hooriaj, Hordaland, Ian Goddard, Ifnord, Iridescent, Ixfd64, J. Ash Bowie, J04n, James Cantor, Jenever Spirit, Jengirl1988, Jfdwolff, Jjkr, Jmh123, Jmm6f488, John Vandenberg, Jonathan B Singer, Jonathan.s.kt, JoshuaEyer, Jrgetsin, Jumbuck, Jérôme Bonnet, Kafziel, Karnarazdan, Katalaveno, Kimiko, Kopaka649, Kshieh, Kukini, Kurykh, Kwertii, Kwjphd, LCP, LSD, LadyofShalott, Leoferretti, Lestrade, Lightmouse, Limegreen, LookingGlass, Lotsofsnails, Malcohol, Maquesta, Marek69, MarionTheLibrarian, Markgodlewski, Marumari, Mattisse, Menelaus2, Mercury, MichaelExe, Mike2vil, Miq, Mirafra, Miroku Sanna, Monado, NRPanikker, NTK, Neutrality, Niels Olson, Niki K, Nneonneo, Noirdame, Obli, Oleg Alexandrov, Olivier, Paul Barlow, Paul Drye, PaulWicks, Pearle, Penbat, Piledhigheranddeeper, Psychonaut, PurpleChez,

PurpleHaze, Quadell, Rab V, Recognizance, RexNL, Riana, Rich Farmbrough, RichardF, RiddledSphinx, Rjwilmsi, Robert K S, Roman à clef, RussellBell, S. M. Sullivan, SJP, Salsb, Sammka, Sandahl, SandyDee, SandyGeorgia, Sardanaphalus, Scarpy, Schlafly, Schrandit, Scuro, Seraphim, Sethmahoney, Sharon Kaplan, Shell Kinney, Signalhead, Simonmatt1100, Sin-man, SiobhanHansa, Smi8900, Snigbrook, Sommers, Sonjaaa, SqueakBox, Standardname, Steph jt, Steve carlson, Sublime98, Suidafrikaan, Super-Magician, Syrthiss, T@Di, Tabletop, Tdowling, Terrek, Thanatosimii, The Anome, Tristanb, Tuesday Star, U10ajf, Ubiq, Uncle G, UnitedStatesian, Utcursch, Uwmad, Vapour, Versus22, Viajero, Vicki Rosenzweig, WLU, WatchAndObserve, WereSpielChequers, WhatamIdoing, Whirlingdervish, Wildt, Wiwaxia, Wolfgang K, Xasodfuih, Xcentaur, Xeryus, Zenohockey, Zeraeph, Zombie-race, 396 anonymous edits

Adult attention deficit hyperactivity disorder *Source*: http://en.wikipedia.org/w/index.php?title=Adult_attention_deficit_hyperactivity_disorder *Contributors*: Addontheweb, Akkhima, Alan Liefting, Alanraywiki, Alarob, Allen3, Annirodgers, Antaeus Feldspar, ArielGold, Avocats, BD2412, Barrylb, Bcjordan, Beetstra, Bellyoffire, Bigbrotheraddicts, Bubba73, CVZ, Catamorphism, Chico349, Chowbok, Computerjoe, Connwriter, Contentmaven, Cooleymd, Creidieki, Curious1i, Cynthiahammer, D6, DAMurphy, DCDuring, Da monster under your bed, DanielCD, Darkfrog24, Dawn Bard, Dewet, DigitalGuy, Dillard421, Doady, EEng, Edwy, FT2, Faduci, Firefoxman, Fuzzform, Ginkgo100, GlassFET, Graham87, Heavensblade23, Hideokun, Hlangeveld, Hordaland, Hyperion35, Itsmejudith, Ivan Matosevic, J.delanoy, Jam osos, Jbeim, Jh12, Jjamison, Jmh649, Johnleemk, Johnuniq, Jojhutton, Jomasecu, Jonverve, KTC, Karn, Keahapana, Kelly Martin, Killiondude, Kingturtle, Kitty the Random, Knighty04, Languorous Lass, Lilac Soul, Literaturegeek, MLauba, Maelwys, MapsMan, Marek69, Markus451, Martijn Hoekstra, Martinog, MattRudd, Mattisse, Mentifisto, Mets501, Michael Hardy, Mjvesuvius, MrJones, MrTroy, Mrshah, Mwanner, Nabokov, Nanite, Navious, NeantHumain, Ned Scott, Nereocystis, Nextdoortoanangel, Nickdc, Nowa, Ofus, Ohnoitsjamie, Oneismany, Open2universe, Owen, PhilipR, Pinkadelica, Pmetzger, QuackGuru, Radon210, Red Act, RedAlgorithm, Richi, Rjwilmsi, Saber girl08, Sannse, Sarah33333, Scuro, Sealauncher, Sfahey, Shrew, Shulae, Sifaka, Silverxxx, Son, Son Goku, Sonjaaa, Spider84, Stdazi, Sticky Parkin, SummerPhD, Tdowling, Tempshill, Terrym2442, The Parting Glass, The Thing That Should Not Be, Theelf29, Thermida, Thexmanlight, Tom, Tom Harris, TooTallSid, Triple-ADHD-AS, Urod, Vaoverland, Versageek, WadeSimMiser, Walshga, Whatever404, Wikivek, Wmahan, 246 anonymous edits

Auditory processing disorder *Source*: http://en.wikipedia.org/w/index.php?title=Auditory_processing_disorder *Contributors*: 1210donna, Altenmann, Aranel, Arcadian, Atheous, Beefcake32, Bemasher, Bonzlee, Brandon.macuser, Bumm13, Chedorlaomer, Codeman38, DJM77bci, DarkFalls, Debresser, Dermal05, Dfruzzetti, Dolfrog, Dome89, ERK, Edward, Elizupp, Eubulides, Fredsmith2, Gatewaycat, Gordonofcartoon, JRDarby, Jusdafax, Karijkindem, Krazyred1988, L'Aquatique, LadyLaurenJayne81, Leon7, Lynch9000s, Mild Bill Hiccup, Minority Report, Orlady, Paul A, Piechjo, Quaeler, Rjwilmsi, Rredfield, SandyGeorgia, Slp1, SteveLoughran, Tomlacroix, Travis.Thurston, Tydoni, Welsh, Whatever404, Woosycat, Yocastal, 60 anonymous edits

Chemical imbalance *Source*: http://en.wikipedia.org/w/index.php?title=Chemical_imbalance *Contributors*: 2over0, AED, AThing, Adashiel, Ahoerstemeier, Alainsarge, Antaeus Feldspar, Aspro, Barrylb, Blingbling1000, CMD Beaker, Cedders, Celebs123, Cesar Tort, Chocolateboy, Claidheamohmor, Coroebus, Cosmic Latte, Crazyvas, Crumbsucker, Davidstrauss, DocJohnny, Eubulides, EyeSerene, Fenke, Fram, Francesca Allan of MindFreedomBC, Freemarket, Fuzzform, Geni, Gerweck, Ground Zero, Heliac, HermesLaoBuddha, Historian932, Iridescent, Jew Aardvark requires assistance with his gas bill lol, Jmh649, John Vandenberg, Jv821, Kbdank71, Limegreen, Longhair, Lupin, Mattisse, Mercury, Metalhead94, Muugokszhiion, Neurodivergent, Nightstallion, Ombudsman, Overtwitch, Pearle, Pol098, Profsnow, RichardF, Rjwilmsi, Rockpocket, Rogerd, Ryulong, Sannse, Scuro, ShadowCreatorII, SilenceDoGood, Ss06470, Standardname, StaticGull, TastyCakes, TheRingess, Tznkai, Voice of All, Wadems, Wknight94, Xyzzyplugh, 113 anonymous edits

Educational psychology *Source*: http://en.wikipedia.org/w/index.php?title=Educational_psychology *Contributors*: 2over0, APH, Aelius28, Aleksd, Aletheia, Ammonius.Grammaticus, Angela, BennettL, Bobo192, Bookandcoffee, BrainDoc, Cabe6403, Choster, Closedmouth, Cmsmith81, CommonsDelinker, Conversion script, Craig.borchardt, Culmensis, Cyanidesandwich, DCDuring, Daven200520, Dbiel, Dcooper, Debresser, DennisDaniels, Dmitri Lytov, Dolfrog, DrGNAGarcia, DustFormsWords, EPM, El C, Encephalon, Epbr123, Espoo, Estill, Fadulj, Florian Huber, Frédérick Lacasse, Gadfium, Geneb1955, GraemeL, Gregbard, Herostratus, Hgilbert, Holon, Hontogaichiban, Icairns, Iss246, Iulus Ascanius, IvyIQTest100, J.delanoy, JCode, Jeff Dahl, JoeSmack, Jokasta, Joyous!, Jtneill, Jusjih, Karol Langner, Kedi the tramp, King of Hearts, Kingfish, Klseifert, Kozuch, LibLord, Lightmouse, Lurene waddell, M.nelson, MGL, Manuel Anastácio, Masterpiece2000, Mattisse, Maxim, McBrayn, Mendaliv, Mercurius, Michael Devore, Michael Hardy, Mingming, Mintleaf, Naddy, Narssarssuaq, Nesbit, Neurolysis, Noe, Nposs, Obesity is really unhealthy!, Outriggr, Phantomsteve, Philip Cross, Prodego, Pustlix Harez, RJFerret, RUL3R, Ral315, RedAlgorithm, Reddi, Reedy, Rhobite, RichardF, Saikiri, SandyGeorgia, Sardanaphalus, Sbirrell, SchoolpsychErin, Schwnj, Seglea, SiobhanHansa, Steinsky, Suisui, Techfiddle, Thesquire, Thiseye, Tim bates, Tomsega, Tony1, Tstrobaugh, Vaughan, Ward3001, WatchAndObserve, Wcquidditch, Whicky1978, Whuitt, Wildt, Zzuuzz, 168 anonymous edits

School psychology *Source*: http://en.wikipedia.org/w/index.php?title=School_psychology *Contributors*: Annapena, Aplarsen, ArglebargleIV, BMF81, CSWarren, Catgut, Chomolungma, Cnota, Dillypickle, Eliyak, Erikj09, Freechild, Frédérick Lacasse, Gpyetter, Ida Shaw, Iss246, IvyIQTest100, J.delanoy, Joeyaa, KeasbeyMornings, Kukini, Louisjkruger, Lova Falk, Maevesinclair, MinerVI, Nesbit, Neutrality, Nosleep, Nposs, NuclearWarfare, Pontificalibus, Sardanaphalus, Sbrools, SchoolpsychErin, Schwnj, Seglea, Sweetsplat, Tdowling, The Thing That Should Not Be, Thingg, Ukexpat, Whicky1978, 70 anonymous edits

Sensory integration dysfunction *Source*: http://en.wikipedia.org/w/index.php?title=Sensory_integration_dysfunction *Contributors*: 23funnel23, A bit iffy, Aaron Brenneman, Aishel, Alensha, Altenmann, Amillar, Arcadian, Aussielocust, Autie62, Baccyak4H, Banjotime, BusterD, Canderson7, Candicejvs, Carolynparrishfan, Cascade1492, Channel4, Charles T. Betz, Cmdrjameson, DB 103245, DanielCD, Eubulides, EurekaLott, Everyking, FloortimeRepository, Hoof Hearted, Insanity Incarnate, J. Van Meter, J04n, Jeremygbyrne, Jkendall13, Jreferee, Kimiko, Kralizec!, LindseyBiel, MCB, MLHarris, MethMan47, Michael Hardy, Mrsdkcrowd, Natski-asnd8, Ojay123, Ombudsman, PWSMom, Pandora, Patrick, Pauljtaylor, Pedneuropsych, Plainpoly, Pne, Polymath618, Psychicbody, R2reming, Rdos, Retodon8, RockMFR, SandyGeorgia, Seraphimblade, Sireebob, Stemcc, Sticky Parkin, SummerPhD, Sweetlipsot, Symphony Girl, TatianaBoshenka, Tcpc13, Tempestt, Terjen, Thorns among our leaves, Tiff31, Traciclem, Verslapper, WLU, WOT, Whatever404, Yocastal, 144 anonymous edits

Sluggish cognitive tempo *Source*: http://en.wikipedia.org/w/index.php?title=Sluggish_cognitive_tempo *Contributors*: *Kat*, AThing, AgentPeppermint, Axiomatica, BMello1618, Banus, Blackirish, Boghog2, Correogsk, DanielCD, Everyking, GregorB, Jonverve, Lova Falk, Max.coke, MaxEnt, MikeVitale, Ojcookies, Pacula, Penbat, Psychonomy, RedAlgorithm, Rich Farmbrough, Rjmooney, Rjwilmsi, S1lenze, Scuro, Shoefly, Sohale, SparsityProblem, Strangedood, Supersymmetry, Tdowling, Triple-Quadruple, Voice of All, WLU, WhatamIdoing, 46 anonymous edits

Wilson's syndrome *Source*: http://en.wikipedia.org/w/index.php?title=Wilson%27s_syndrome *Contributors*: Alterrabe, Collectonian, Digfarenough, Diogenes969, John Nevard, Kenosis, KillerChihuahua, MastCell, Maungataniwha, MedBoard, MedBoard2, Orangemarlin, Orlady, Pcblue, Rjm at sleepers, Samwhite006, SandyGeorgia, Sohale, Sticky Parkin, Vermontpancakeeater, WhatamIdoing, WriterHound, Zumost, 4 anonymous edits

Image Sources, Licenses and Contributors

GNU Free Documentation License Version 1.2, November 2002 Copyright (C) 2000,2001,2002 Free Software Foundation, Inc. 59 Temple Place, Suite 330, Boston, MA 02111-1307 USA Everyone is permitted to copy and distribute verbatim copies of this license document, but changing it is not allowed.

0. PREAMBLE

The purpose of this License is to make a manual, textbook, or other functional and useful document "free" in the sense of freedom: to assure everyone the effective freedom to copy and redistribute it, with or without modifying it, either commercially or noncommercially. Secondarily, this License preserves for the author and publisher a way to get credit for their work, while not being considered responsible for modifications made by others. This License is a kind of "copyleft", which means that derivative works of the document must themselves be free in the same sense. It complements the GNU General Public License, which is a copyleft license designed for free software. We have designed this License in order to use it for manuals for free software, because free software needs free documentation: a free program should come with manuals providing the same freedoms that the software does. But this License is not limited to software manuals; it can be used for any textual work, regardless of subject matter or whether it is published as a printed book. We recommend this License principally for works whose purpose is instruction or reference.

1. APPLICABILITY AND DEFINITIONS

This License applies to any manual or other work, in any medium, that contains a notice placed by the copyright holder saying it can be distributed under the terms of this License. Such a notice grants a world-wide, royalty-free license, unlimited in duration, to use that work under the conditions stated herein. The "Document", below, refers to any such manual or work. Any member of the public is a licensee, and is addressed as "you". You accept the license if you copy, modify or distribute the work in a way requiring permission under copyright law. A "Modified Version" of the Document means any work containing the Document or a portion of it, either copied verbatim, or with modifications and/or translated into another language. A "Secondary Section" is a named appendix or a front-matter section of the Document that deals exclusively with the relationship of the publishers or authors of the Document to the Document's overall subject (or to related matters) and contains nothing that could fall directly within that overall subject. (Thus, if the Document is in part a textbook of mathematics, a Secondary Section may not explain any mathematics.) The relationship could be a matter of historical connection with the subject or with related matters, or of legal, commercial, philosophical, ethical or political position regarding them. The "Invariant Sections" are certain Secondary Sections whose titles are designated, as being those of Invariant Sections, in the notice that says that the Document is released under this License. If a section does not fit the above definition of Secondary then it is not allowed to be designated as Invariant. The Document may contain zero Invariant Sections. If the Document does not identify any Invariant Sections then there are none. The "Cover Texts" are certain short passages of text that are listed, as Front-Cover Texts or Back-Cover Texts, in the notice that says that the Document is released under this License. A Front-Cover Text may be at most 5 words, and a Back-Cover Text may be at most 25 words. A "Transparent" copy of the Document means a machine-readable copy, represented in a format whose specification is available to the general public, that is suitable for revising the document straightforwardly with generic text editors or (for images composed of pixels) generic paint programs or (for drawings) some widely available drawing editor, and that is suitable for input to text formatters or for automatic translation to a variety of formats suitable for input to text formatters. A copy made in an otherwise Transparent file format whose markup, or absence of markup, has been arranged to thwart or discourage subsequent modification by readers is not Transparent. An image format is not Transparent if used for any substantial amount of text. A copy that is not "Transparent" is called "Opaque". Examples of suitable formats for Transparent copies include plain ASCII without markup, Texinfo input format, LaTeX input format, SGML or XML using a publicly available DTD, and standard-conforming simple HTML, PostScript or PDF designed for human modification. Examples of transparent image formats include PNG, XCF and JPG. Opaque formats include proprietary formats that can be read and edited only by proprietary word processors, SGML or XML for which the DTD and/or processing tools are not generally available, and the machine-generated HTML, PostScript or PDF produced by some word processors for output purposes only. The "Title Page" means, for a printed book, the title page itself, plus such following pages as are needed to hold, legibly, the material this License requires to appear in the title page. For works in formats which do not have any title page as such, "Title Page" means the text near the most prominent appearance of the work's title, preceding the beginning of the body of the text. A section "Entitled XYZ" means a named subunit of the Document whose title either is precisely XYZ or contains XYZ in parentheses following text that translates XYZ in another language. (Here XYZ stands for a specific section name mentioned below, such as "Acknowledgements", "Dedications", "Endorsements", or "History".) To "Preserve the Title" of such a section when you modify the Document means that it remains a section "Entitled XYZ" according to this definition. The Document may include Warranty Disclaimers next to the notice which states that this License applies to the Document. These Warranty Disclaimers are considered to be included by reference in this License, but only as regards disclaiming warranties: any other implication that these Warranty Disclaimers may have is void and has no effect on the meaning of this License.

2. VERBATIM COPYING

You may copy and distribute the Document in any medium, either commercially or noncommercially, provided that this License, the copyright notices, and the license notice saying this License applies to the Document are reproduced in all copies, and that you add no other conditions whatsoever to those of this License. You may not use technical measures to obstruct or control the reading or further copying of the copies you make or distribute. However, you may accept compensation in exchange for copies. If you distribute a large enough number of copies you must also follow the conditions in section 3. You may also lend copies, under the same conditions stated above, and you may publicly display copies.

3. COPYING IN QUANTITY

If you publish printed copies (or copies in media that commonly have printed covers) of the Document, numbering more than 100, and the Document's license notice requires Cover Texts, you must enclose the copies in covers that carry, clearly and legibly, all these Cover Texts: Front-Cover Texts on the front cover, and Back-Cover Texts on the back cover. Both covers must also clearly and legibly identify you as the publisher of these copies. The front cover must present the full title with all words of the title equally prominent and visible. You may add other material on the covers in addition. Copying with changes limited to the covers, as long as they preserve the title of the Document and satisfy these conditions, can be treated as verbatim copying in other respects. If the required texts for either cover are too voluminous to fit legibly, you should put the first ones listed (as many as fit reasonably) on the actual cover, and continue the rest onto adjacent pages. If you publish or distribute Opaque copies of the Document numbering more than 100, you must either include a machine-readable Transparent copy along with each Opaque copy, or state in or with each Opaque copy a computer-network location from which the general network-using public has access to download using public-standard network protocols a complete Transparent copy of the Document, free of added material. If you use the latter option, you must take reasonably prudent steps, when you begin distribution of Opaque copies in quantity, to ensure that this Transparent copy will remain thus accessible at the stated location until at least one year after the last time you distribute an Opaque copy (directly or through your agents or retailers) of that edition to the public. It is requested, but not required, that you contact the authors of the Document well before redistributing any large number of copies, to give them a chance to provide you with an updated version of the Document.

4. MODIFICATIONS

You may copy and distribute a Modified Version of the Document under the conditions of sections 2 and 3 above, provided that you release the Modified Version under precisely this License, with the Modified Version filling the role of the Document, thus licensing distribution and modification of the Modified Version to whoever possesses a copy of it. In addition, you must do these things in the Modified Version: A. Use in the Title Page (and on the covers, if any) a title distinct from that of the Document, and from those of previous versions (which should, if there were any, be listed in the History section of the Document). You may use the same title as a previous version if the original publisher of that version gives permission. B. List on the Title Page, as authors, one or more persons or entities responsible for authorship of the modifications in the Modified Version, together with at least five of the principal authors of the Document (all of its principal authors, if it has fewer than five), unless they release you from this requirement. C. State on the Title page the name of the publisher of the Modified Version, as the publisher. D. Preserve all the copyright notices of the Document. E. Add an appropriate copyright notice for your modifications adjacent to the other copyright notices. F. Include, immediately after the copyright notices, a license notice giving the public permission to use the Modified Version under the terms of this License, in the form shown in the Addendum below. G. Preserve in that license notice the full lists of Invariant Sections and required Cover Texts given in the Document's license notice. H. Include an unaltered copy of this License. I. Preserve the section Entitled "History", Preserve its Title, and add to it an item stating at least the title, year, new authors, and publisher of the Modified Version as given on the Title Page. If there is no section Entitled "History" in the Document, create one stating the title, year, authors, and publisher of the Document as given on its Title Page, then add an item describing the Modified Version as stated in the previous sentence. J. Preserve the network location, if any, given in the Document for public access to a Transparent copy of the Document, and likewise the network locations given in the Document for previous versions it was based on. These may be placed in the "History" section. You may omit a network location for a work that was published at least four years before the Document itself, or if the original publisher of the version it refers to gives permission. K. For any section Entitled "Acknowledgements" or "Dedications", Preserve the Title of the section, and preserve in the section all the substance and tone of each of the contributor acknowledgements and/or dedications given therein. L. Preserve all the Invariant Sections of the Document, unaltered in their text and in their titles. Section numbers or the equivalent are not considered part of the section titles. M. Delete any section Entitled "Endorsements". Such a section may not be included in the Modified Version. N. Do not retitle any existing section to be Entitled "Endorsements" or to conflict in title with any Invariant Section. O. Preserve any Warranty Disclaimers. If the Modified Version includes new front-matter sections or appendices that qualify as Secondary Sections and contain no material copied from the Document, you may at your option designate some or all of these sections as invariant. To do this, add their titles to the list of Invariant Sections in the Modified Version's license notice. These titles must be distinct from any other section titles. You may add a section Entitled "Endorsements", provided it contains nothing but endorsements of your Modified Version by various parties--for example, statements of peer review or that the text has been approved by an organization as the authoritative definition of a standard. You may add a passage of up to five words as a Front-Cover Text, and a passage of up to 25 words as a Back-Cover Text, to the end of the list of Cover Texts in the Modified Version. Only one passage of Front-Cover Text and one of Back-Cover Text may be added by (or through arrangements made by) any one entity. If the Document already includes a cover text for the same cover, previously added by you or by arrangement made by the same entity you are acting on behalf of, you may not add another; but you may replace the old one, on explicit permission from the previous publisher that added the old one. The author(s) and publisher(s) of the Document do not by this License give permission to use their names for publicity for or to assert or imply endorsement of any Modified Version.

5. COMBINING DOCUMENTS

You may combine the Document with other documents released under this License, under the terms defined in section 4 above for modified versions, provided that you include in the combination all of the Invariant Sections of all of the original documents, unmodified, and list them all as Invariant Sections of your combined work in its license notice, and that you preserve all their Warranty Disclaimers. The combined work need only contain one copy of this License, and multiple identical Invariant Sections may be replaced with a single copy. If there are multiple Invariant Sections with the same name but different contents, make the title of each such section unique by adding at the end of it, in parentheses, the name of the original author or publisher of that section if known, or else a unique number. Make the same adjustment to the section titles in the list of Invariant Sections in the license notice of the combined work. In the combination, you must combine any sections Entitled "History" in the various original documents, forming one section Entitled "History"; likewise combine any sections Entitled "Acknowledgements", and any sections Entitled "Dedications". You must delete all sections Entitled "Endorsements".

6. COLLECTIONS OF DOCUMENTS

You may make a collection consisting of the Document and other documents released under this License, and replace the individual copies of this License in the various documents with a single copy that is included in the collection, provided that you follow the rules of this License for verbatim copying of each of the documents in all other respects. You may extract a single document from such a collection, and distribute it individually under this License, provided you insert a copy of this License into the extracted document, and follow this License in all other respects regarding verbatim copying of that document.

7. AGGREGATION WITH INDEPENDENT WORKS

A compilation of the Document or its derivatives with other separate and independent documents or works, in or on a volume of a storage or distribution medium, is called an "aggregate" if the copyright resulting from the compilation is not used to limit the legal rights of the compilation's users beyond what the individual works permit. When the Document is included in an aggregate, this License does not apply to the other works in the aggregate which are not themselves derivative works of the Document. If the Cover Text requirement of section 3 is applicable to these copies of the Document, then if the Document is less than one half of the entire aggregate, the Document's Cover Texts may be placed on covers that bracket the Document within the aggregate, or the electronic equivalent of covers if the Document is in electronic form. Otherwise they must appear on printed covers that bracket the whole aggregate.

8. TRANSLATION

Translation is considered a kind of modification, so you may distribute translations of the Document under the terms of section 4. Replacing Invariant Sections with translations requires special permission from their copyright holders, but you may include translations of some or all Invariant Sections in addition to the original versions of these Invariant Sections. You may include a translation of this License, and all the license notices in the Document, and any Warranty Disclaimers, provided that you also include the original English version of this License and the original versions of those notices and disclaimers. In case of a disagreement between the translation and the original version of this License or a notice or disclaimer, the original version will prevail. If a section in the Document is Entitled "Acknowledgements", "Dedications", or "History", the requirement (section 4) to Preserve its Title (section 1) will typically require changing the actual title.

9. TERMINATION

You may not copy, modify, sublicense, or distribute the Document except as expressly provided for under this License. Any other attempt to copy, modify, sublicense or distribute the Document is void, and will automatically terminate your rights under this License. However, parties who have received copies, or rights, from you under this License will not have their licenses terminated so long as such parties remain in full compliance.

10. FUTURE REVISIONS OF THIS LICENSE

The Free Software Foundation may publish new, revised versions of the GNU Free Documentation License from time to time. Such new versions will be similar in spirit to the present version, but may differ in detail to address new problems or concerns. See http://www.gnu.org/copyleft/. Each version of the License is given a distinguishing version number. If the Document specifies that a particular numbered version of this License "or any later version" applies to it, you have the option of following the terms and conditions either of that specified version or of any later version that has been published (not as a draft) by the Free Software Foundation. If the Document does not specify a version number of this License, you may choose any version ever published (not as a draft) by the Free Software Foundation. ADDENDUM: How to use this License for your documents To use this License in a document you have written, include a copy of the License in the document and put the following copyright and license notices just after the title page: Copyright (c) YEAR YOUR NAME. Permission is granted to copy, distribute and/or modify this document under the terms of the GNU Free Documentation License, Version 1.2 or any later version published by the Free Software Foundation; with no Invariant Sections, no Front-Cover Texts, and no Back-Cover Texts. A copy of the license is included in the section entitled "GNU Free Documentation License". If you have Invariant Sections, Front-Cover Texts and Back-Cover Texts, replace the "with...Texts." line with this: with the Invariant Sections being LIST THEIR TITLES, with the Front-Cover Texts being LIST, and with the Back-Cover Texts being LIST. If you have Invariant Sections without Cover Texts, or some other combination of the three, merge those two alternatives to suit the situation. If your document contains nontrivial examples of program code, we recommend releasing these examples in parallel under your choice of free software license, such as the GNU General Public License, to permit their use in free software.

Made in the USA
Lexington, KY
25 January 2010